Tales of Immortals

Compiled by Yuan Yang

Foreign Languages Press   Beijing

First Edition 2000
Second Printing 2010

ISBN 978-7-119-02142-3

© Foreign Languages Press, Beijing, China, 2010

Published by Foreign Languages Press

24 Baiwanzhuang Road, Beijing 100037, China

http://www.flp.com.cn

Distributed by China International Book Trading Corporation

35 Chegongzhuang Xilu, Beijing 100044, China

P.O. Box 399, Beijing, China

Printed in the People's Republic of China

Contents

Yu the Great Finds a Wife

During the reign of the sage emperor Shun, about 4,000 years ago, the world was afflicted by disastrous floods. A hero called Yu succeeded in taming the troublesome waters, bringing tranquillity to the people. However, he had been so busy with his flood-fighting task that he had no time to seek a wife. One day, having climbed to the summit of Mount Tushan (Mount Dangtu in Anhui Province) to survey a river course, it suddenly struck him that he was already over 30 years old but had not yet found a wife. So he prayed to Heaven to send him a mate.

Since the sun was setting in the west he stayed overnight on the mountain. At the stroke of midnight a white fox with nine tails paced around the rude hut where he lay. When he saw this fox he said to himself: "White is the color of my clothes, and nine tails signify that I will become a king." Thereupon, he sang the Song of Tushan:

A white fox with nine tails has appeared by my side.
How happy I'll be with a beauty for a wife,

When husband and wife work together with one heart.

Then harmony rules between Heaven and man.

As soon as he finished singing, the white fox turned into a beautiful girl. Yu married the girl and gave her the name Nü Jiao.

Because of his achievements in taming the floods, Yu won high esteem among the people and succeeded Shun to the rule of All Under Heaven. He is known to history as Yu the Great. Qi, Yu's son, established the Xia Dynasty (c. 21st-16th centuries B.C.), the first dynasty in China's history.

From *Annals of the States of Wu and Yue*

The Vision of Yunmeng Pool

King Xiang of Chu (298-263 B.C.) went to Yunmeng Pool (north of Jianli, in Hubei Province) for outing together with the scholar Song Yu. There was a building named Gaotang in the distance. It was enshrouded in swirling clouds which were continually changing their appearance.

King Xiang was fascinated by the clouds, and asked Song Yu about this mysterious phenomenon.

Song Yu replied, "Some time ago the late king spent the night in Gaotang. He dreamed that a beautiful girl came to him and said, 'I am the daughter of Mount Wushan. I heard that Your Majesty was here. So I would like to keep you company.'

"In the morning, just as the girl was planning to leave, the king wished to detain her. But she said, 'I live at the south foot of Mount Wushan. In the morning, I appear as the rosy clouds of dawn, while in the evening I turn into drizzle. Stand on the balcony morning and evening, and that is the way we can meet.'

"The next morning the king went out onto the balcony. It was really like what the goddess said.

3

Therefore, the late king had a temple built for her, and named it Zhaoyun (Morning Clouds)."

King Xiang of Chu asked, "What does the goddess look like today?"

Song Yu replied, "When the goddess appears she raises her long, wide green sleeve to shade herself from the sunlight and yearns for her lover. Sometimes she rides a fast chariot decorated with flags and colorful feathers. She rides back and forth, accompanied sometimes by winds, sometimes by drizzle. If wind and drizzle stop, the goddess does not know the direction in which she should go."

Hearing this, King Xiang asked: "May I go to visit Mount Wushan?"

Song Yu said: "Of course."

Then King Xiang said: "Tell me about Gaotang."

"Gaotang is located on an immensely high cliff," said the other. "Standing there and gazing far into the distance you can enjoy a beautiful view, with water flowing below your feet and the blue sky above your head. There are wonderful natural phenomena around you which are beyond description." Song Yu said.

"But can you describe it in general?" asked King Xiang.

"Yes, Your Majesty." Song Yu said. "The other mountains can't be mentioned in the same breath as Mount Wushan, where Gaotang is located. There is a pool on the mountain, where the water is always fresh after rain. The streams of the valley all join together here, and then surge away in all directions. Range upon range of hills are battered by the roaring waters. The water flows rapidly around the hills with waves breaking and foaming, and looking like clouds floating freely. What a beautiful sight!"

"Looking down at the valley from the high hills, it is green all the time. The hazel trees are emerald green, with an exuberant growth of branches, leaves and flowers. Their branches sway gently in the breeze and stretch in all directions, like birds flapping their wings. The wind soughs like an ancient musical instrument, clear but sonorous and low but deep. When people hear this sound they are overcome with excitement. But when orphans and widows hear the sound their hearts will tremble and tears roll from their eyes; and those who are frustrated in their careers will feel gloomy and sigh all the time."

King Xiang was moved and asked Song Yu: "When the late king was there, what did he do?"

Song Yu said, "The late king sauntered by the meandering streams and met the alchemists Xian Men and Gao Shi in the green mountains, and took them with him. Then the late king toured in a carriage inlaid by jade and driven by a hornless dragon. There were many flags along the way and everyone was happy and gay. When they arrived at Yunmen, the king dismounted and went hunting. He ordered his servants to stay where they were, and he walked around the pool."

As King Xiang listened to this, he was as if intoxicated with wonder. Then he asked Song Yu: "Is it possible for me to go to Gaotang?"

Song Yu nodded, and said with a smile: "If Your Majesty wants to meet the goddess of Mount Wushan you should abstain from meat and have peace of mind. Then we'll choose a lucky day to go. You will not only meet the goddess, but will live a long life."

From *The Elegies of Chu • On Gaotang*

The Goddess of Mount Wushan

That night, after relating the story of the goddess of Mount Wushan, the goddess appeared to Song Yu in a dream. The next day, when he presented himself at court, he told the king his dream. The king was fascinated, and questioned him closely. Song Yu explained, "When I went back home that day I was in a disturbed state of mind and had a premonition that something would happen. I went to bed and immediately fell sound asleep. I dreamed that I climbed Mount Wushan and entered Gaotang. Suddenly, a very beautiful girl appeared before me. When I tried to speak to her I woke up with a start. Sadly I pondered, and eventually I realized that the girl was the goddess whom the late king had met."

The King asked hurriedly: "What did she look like?"

Song Yu said: "She is very pretty and is of all fine qualities of women. No one in history can be compared with her. She looks like the sun when you see her in the distance and like the moon when you see her close up. She has a gentle disposition and an easy manner. She makes men relaxed and joyful."

7

King Xiang was so spellbound by this account of the beautiful girl that he urged Song Yu to tell him more."

The other continued, "The goddess is natural, dignified and quiet. She has a graceful carriage and her complexion is like a spring peach. Her eyes are as clear as water, and are framed by black, long and thin eyebrows, curling at the edges. Her lips are as red as vermilion. I peeped at her while she was sitting in her carriage, and she also looked at me through the curtain. It seemed that she was there to meet somebody. But when I went up to her carriage and lifted the curtain she wouldn't look at me. I poured out my admiration to her. Finally she talked to me. We gradually came to understood each other and were very happy. But before we finished our talk she suddenly became little angry and ordered her servants to take her home. I stayed there to see her off, and she gave me an affectionate backward glance. I said sincerely: "I will never forget our meeting, although it was a brief one." She was embarrassed, and left reluctantly.

After the goddess left I was depressed and distracted. I even didn't know where I was. Then I woke up and thought of the goddess till dawn.

Hearing that, King Xiang laughed and said, "That means that there will be another meeting between the two of you."

From *Elegies of Chu* • *On the Goddess*

Kua Fu Chases the Sun

Long, long ago, there was an immortal named Kua Fu living in the area of Zaitian Mountain near present-day Chengdu. With a yellow snake hanging from each ear and a yellow snake in each hand Kua Fu ran very fast. He looked like he was flying when he ran. He told people that he could run so fast that he could catch up the sun.

Once, he ran after the sun from morning till dusk. When he reached the place where the sun was setting his lips were dry and his mouth was parched. It seemed that there was fire in his throat. So he went to the Weihe River in present-day Shaanxi Province for a drink of water. He drank greedily till the river dried up. But he was still thirsty. Then he went straight to the north to find more water to drink, but died on the way. He left his stick by the roadside, which later became a vast forest.

From *The Classic of Mountains and Rivers*

Two Girls on the Yangtze River

Long, long ago, people often saw two beautiful girls strolling by the Yangtze River. Nobody knew where they came from.

One day, when the two girls were taking a walk along the Hanshui River, the largest branch of the Yangtze, they were overtaken by Zheng Jiaopu and his servant in a fine carriage. Zheng was young and frivolous by nature. When he saw the two beautiful girls he was overcome by desire. But little did he know that they were in fact immortals. Zheng Jiaopu said to his servant: "I want to have their jade ornaments as souvenirs, so that I can get to know them."

His servant tried to dissuade him, saying, "People here have glib tongues. If you fail to achieve your goal you will make yourself a laughing stock. Then you'll find it too late for regrets."

Zheng ignored his servant's advice, and went straight up to the two girls and said, "You must have had a tiring journey."

The two girls answered him: "We have not, but you must be tired after your journey."

Thereupon, Zheng recited the rhythmic lines: "I put oranges into a square basket and let it flow along the Hanshui River. I walk along the river and drink the orange juice."

He continued: "You can see that I talk freely and without any inhibition. To tell you the truth, I want your jade ornaments."

The two girls showed no sign of annoyance at this abrupt request, but repeated, "I put oranges into a round basket and let it flow along the Hanshui River. I walk along the river and drink the orange juice."

Then they took off their jade ornaments and gave them to Zheng. Zheng snatched them and stuffed them inside his gown. He rushed away with his booty, and dozens of yards further on he stopped to examine his newly-acquired treasures. But, lo and behold! — they had vanished into thin air! Puzzled, Zheng glanced back, only to find that the two girls had vanished.

From *Accounts of the Saints* • *The Two Girls by the Yangtze River*

The Water Goddess Mi Fei

One day in the third year of Huang Chu (222), Cao Zijian (Cao Zhi), who had lost out to his brother, Cao Pei, Emperor Wendi of Wu, in the competition to succeed to their father's throne, left Luoyang, the capital, for his own fief. On his way he passed Mount Jueshan, crossed the Xuanyuan Mountains and traversed the vast valley beyond them. When he finally reached the Jingshan Mountains the sun was sinking in the west. He and his party were tired, so they made camp for the night.

As dusk fell Zijian walked down the hill to the bank of the Luoshui River, (the present-day Luohe River in Henan Province). He stood silently gazing at the river for a long time. It seemed that he was waiting for something to happen.... Suddenly he saw a beautiful girl standing on the far bank. Then, in an instant she had vanished. Calling to his carriage driver, who had followed him at a discreet distance, he asked, "Did you see a beautiful girl standing over there just now?"

The carriage driver looked at the spot where Zijian was pointing and shook his head. "I didn't see anything," he said. "But I was told that there is a goddess who lives in the Luoshui River, named Mi Fei. It is possible that she was the vision you saw just now. What did she look like?"

Zijian thought for a moment, and then said, "She had a graceful bearing and easy manner. She was soft but full of vigor. In the distance, she looked like the sun in the rosy dawn while from nearby she looked like a lotus just risen from clear water."

As he said this, a feeling of sadness suddenly came over Zijian, and he choked on his words. Seeing this, the driver stole away, leaving Zijian immersed in bittersweet memories.

Exactly one year before to the day, Cao Zhijian had passed the Luoshui River on his way from the capital. Gazing pensively at the river, Zijian suddenly saw a beautiful girl appeared in the mist and floated to the place where he was standing. It was the water goddess Mi Fei.

The goddess looked very beautiful, with ice-like skin, arched eyebrows and her hair done up in a bun on top of her head. When she smiled her cheeks dimpled in a most charming way.

As soon as Zijian saw her he was wild with joy. The two of them—a goddess and mortal man—fell instantly in love. They exchanged jade pendants as love tokens, and Mi Fei offered to take Zijian to her Water Palace. Just at that moment the young man remembered an ancient story of how Zheng Jiaopu met a fairy beauty by the Hanshui River. They too had exchanged pendants as love tokens, but after that nobody knew what happened to Zheng Jiaopu. So Zijian hesitated, overcome with trepidation.

When the Goddess of the Luoshui River noticed his reticence. She was rather disappointed that Zijian did not trust her. She felt sad and heaved a deep sigh. Just at that time the waves rose in the river. When the gods of the water heard Mi Fei's sigh they gathered at her side to discuss something with her. Then the goddess pulled Zijian and took him flying above the waves.

At that time, the wind dropped and the waves subsided. Zijian and the Goddess sat face to face and strains of music were heard accompanied by drumbeats. Fishes jumped out of the water and danced accompanied by the birds in the sky. The water gods congratulated Zijian and Mi Fei, and sang and danced to their hearts' content. After that, Zijian and Mi Fei mounted a cloud-chariot pulled by six dragons and guarded by whales. They traveled the length and breadth of the earth and the sky.

Finally, the cloud-chariot landed on Jingshan Ridge. There the goddess told Zijian that the two would have to part, as she was destined to live beneath the waves, while he, a mortal, was fated to live on dry land. Mounting the cloud-chariot, Mi Fei flew away.

After that, Zijian often returned to the Luoshui

River, lingering on its banks or floating in a boat on its waters, hoping for just one more glimpse of his fairy lover. But the goddess and the mortal never met again.

From *Collected Works of Cao Zijian* •
The Goddess of the Luoshui River

The Yellow Emperor Battles Chi You

It is said that about 4,000 or 5,000 years ago the Yellow Emperor succeeded in unifying the various tribes into which the Chinese people were divided only after defeating a monster named Chi You. Chi You had 81 henchmen who had man-shaped heads but the bodies of beasts. Their heads were made of bronze and their foreheads of iron. They ate stones and sand. They were good at making weapons, such as clubs, swords, spears, and bows and arrows.

The people begged the Yellow Emperor to rid the world of the scourge of Chi You. Nine times did the Yellow Emperor fight Chi You and his men, but was defeated every time. He fled to Mount Taishan, where he hid himself away, disconsolate. One day, a creature with a woman's head and a bird's body appeared before him and said, "I am the Goddess of the Nine Heavens. Tell me why you hide yourself here in despair."

The Yellow Emperor threw himself to his knees in front of the goddess, and explained how the people, groaning under the tyranny of Chi You, had asked him to deliver them. "But in nine battles I failed to overcome the monster and his band of fiends," he lamented.

The goddess thereupon gave the Yellow Emperor a magic talisman. Bearing this talisman on high, the Yellow Emperor once more engaged Chi You in battle at Qingqiu. This time he was victorious, and Chi You and his cohorts were slain.

The Yellow Emperor went on to unite the tribes under his rule. When they grew restive, he displayed pictures of Chi You to frighten them. In this way the Yellow Emperor became the ancestor of the Chinese race.

From *Imperial Digest of the Taiping Reign Period*

Bringing the Stone Men Back to Life

During the reign of Emperor Xuandi (73-49 B.C.) of the Han Dynasty two men bound in chains were discovered in a cave in the Shushu Mountains. The people who discovered them were curious, and took them to the capital, Chang'an. But just before they reached the city, the two men turned into stone. Emperor Xuandi was surprised to hear about this, and asked his advisors what it meant. Only Liu Xiang, a learned minister, ventured an opinion: "They are disloyal ministers of the ancient State of Yayu, Your Majesty. For some serious crime they were enchained in that cave until an enlightened emperor should learn of their plight and release them."

The emperor, however, suspected Liu Xiang's motive for saying this, and had him thrown into prison.

Liu Xiang's son, Liu Xin, consulted his father as to the best way to convince the emperor that he was telling the truth. His father said, "The only way is to bring those two stone men back to life."

Liu Xin thereupon went to the emperor, and said, "If the two stone men are fed the milk of a seven-year old girl, Your Majesty, they will come back to life."

The emperor, though doubtful, had this done, and, sure enough, the stone men came back to life.

They thanked emperor and related what had happened to them. As their account tallied with Liu Xiang's theory, the emperor made the latter a senior official, and bestowed appropriate honor upon his son. Then the emperor asked them: "How do you know this?"

They replied, "The story can be found in *The Classic of Mountains and Rivers.*

From then on, *The Classic of Mountains and Rivers* was read widely at the emperor's court.

From *Records of Strange Things and People*

20

Nüwa and the Beginning of Matrilineal Society

Nüwa was a divine woman who patched the holes in the sky with stone blocks. When Earth was first separated from Heaven there were only two people at that time — Nüwa and her brother. They lived in the Kunlun Mountains in northwest China. In order to create mankind, Nüwa and her brother married, so as to produce progeny. But they felt ashamed. So they prayed to Heaven, as follows:

"If Heaven agrees that we, sister and brother, can be husband and wife, the clouds in the sky should be together. If Heaven does not agree, the clouds should all be separated."

Finishing their prayer, they suddenly saw the clouds moving. Before long, all the clouds in the sky had combined into one solid mass. The brother and sister took this as a sign of approval from Heaven, and decided to get married.

On their wedding day they made a fan out of cogongrass to hide their faces because they felt ashamed.

The saying "round fan, round fan, used for beauties to hide their faces" originated from this story. Later on, when girls felt ashamed, they always hid their faces behind fans.

From *Records of Strange Things and People*

A Water Fairy

Zhang Yu lived in Luoyang, the capital. He was used to a dissolute life with other rich young idlers. One spring day, he was walking alone by the Luochuan River. The scenery was charming, the fragrance of the flowers was intoxicating, and the singing of the birds in the trees was delightful. Fish leaped out of the quiet water from time to time. Zhang Yu couldn't help reciting aloud:

This fleeting life of ours like a dream,
There is a great deal of hardship in one's short
*   life.*
But no one can tell me how to live longer,
I can only sing a song by the Luochuan River in
*   spring.*

As soon as he finished, he saw a green tent erected on the bank, with clear and melodious music coming from it. Zhang Yu was surprised, and wondered to himself: "Who on the earth has come here for spring outing?" Just then a pretty girl left the tent and walked slowly along the bank, reciting poetry all the while. Zhang Yu, having a dissolute disposition, went up boldly to the girl and asked,

23

"Where are you from, young lady, the Heaven or Penglai, the island of immortals?"

That gave the girl a start, and it was some time before she recovered her composure. Then she said, "How dare you, young man, interrupt me while I am reciting poetry?"

Zhang Yu replied, "Forgive me, but I like reading poems too. When I heard you reciting I couldn't help stopping to listen."

Hearing that, the girl smiled and pointed to the tent. "Please be so kind as to accompany me for a little refreshment," she said.

Following the girl, Zhang Yu entered the tent. The girl ordered her servants to lay a feast, accompanied by music. The two talked and laughed cheerfully, and feasted till sunset. The girl said: "Life is short. As soon as the spring is gone, autumn is here. A young man becomes old in the twinkling of an eye. People who understand this principle understand each other."

At this Zhang Yu lowered his head and didn't say anything. Then the girl recited:

Colorful clouds float in the sky,
The white crane flies back again.
It is impossible to stay longer here,
But we can stay in Penglai, the Island of the
*   immortals forever.*

She continued:

It is useless to love the trees, which live forever,

Because they are not long-living people.
Today we say goodbye on the bank of the
*   Luochuan River,*
It is a pity we will not see each other next
*   spring.*

Then the girl said goodbye to Zhang Yu, and floated away along the surface of the river. The astonished Zhang Yu was convinced that the girl must be a water fairy.

From *Strange Stories of Immortals*

The Girl Piper on the Bank
of the Hanshui River

It was said that a girl, some 17 or 18 years old, was often seen on the bank of the Hanshui River in the morning or evening and played on a reed pipe. She was very beautiful and always wore green clothes. She had a boat in the river and when she saw people coming she would jump into the boat. Sometimes she appeared once a year, sometimes once a month.

One year during the Tianbao period (742-756) of the Tang Dynasty a dissolute young man named Wang Yi heard that story and, filled with curiosity, left the capital, Chang'an, and went in search of her. He waited on the riverbank for many days but the girl did not show up. Just as he was about to leave, disappointed, the girl in her boat appeared, with the reed pipe in her hand. She disembarked and played at the waterside. Wang Yi was wild with joy. He ran to the girl and said, "Who are you waiting for, here by the Hanshui River, immortal?"

The girl turned to look at Wang Yi, and said, with a smile: "I'm waiting for you."

Wang Yi said, "I didn't know that you were

waiting for me for so many years. I have long been tired of the life of ordinary people. I am eager to cast off this mundane existence."

The girl told him: "Don't be reluctant to leave the mortal world. You will scarcely have time to your early youth before you will become old. Then you'll die. Such a life can't be compared to the life of immortals living on Penglai Island. The immortals live in golden and silver palaces, without any worries. When they go out they ride cranes and phoenixes. They rest in fields full of the herbs of immortality and banquet by Jasper Lake, the dwelling place of the Queen Mother of the West. The immortals will never become old and die."

As Wang Yi heard that he laughed: "May I be your slave and carry your pipe?"

With a smile, the girl said, "You don't even know! You have been a slave for many years already."

Saying that, she instructed Wang Yi to enter the boat with her. Then the boat sailed away.

After many days, people again saw the girl and Wang Yi at the riverside. Wang Yi told the people: "Please tell the young people in Chang'an that I went away with the girl who plays the reed pipe, and will never return to Chang'an." Then he and the girl entered the boat again and left. They never returned to the riverside, and nobody knew where they went.

From *Strange Stories of Immortals*

Liu Shi and Yuan Che Pass
on a Treasure

During the Yuanhe period (806-820) of the reign of Emperor Xianzong of the Tang Dynasty two young men from official families of Hengshan went to Lingnan on business. On their way back, they prepared to spend the night in a boat moored at a riverbank in Baipu County, Lianzhou Prefecture. Suddenly a gale sprang up, the mooring cable broke and the boat drifted with the tide. After half an hour the gale stopped suddenly and the moon came out. The two young men came out of the cabin and found that the boat had drifted to an isolated island. They could not see any houses, only a Taoist temple. They went in, and saw incense burning in front of a jade statue of the Celestial Worthy in the main hall. They wondered who had come to burn incense, since the island seemed to be uninhabited. Just then, two maidservants entered the temple, one holding a jade case and the other a golden stove. They burned more incense before the statue and prepared to leave. The young men went up to them and kowtowed. They told them what had happened to them, whereupon the maidservants said, "Yu Xu, the priest, will be here soon; he may be able to help you."

No sooner had they finished saying this when a priest, riding a deer and crowned with clouds, dropped down from the sky and alighted at the temple. The young men hurriedly turned to the newcomer for help. The priest instructed the maidservants to take them to Lady Nan Ming (South Sea).

Lady Nan Ming was, in fact, a girl of about 15 years old, gorgeously attired. She said with a smile: "Liu Shi and Yuan Che, you have come at the right time. This must have been arranged by the Heaven?"

Then she asked the maidservants: "Did they come in a carriage?"

The maids answered: "No, they came across Baihua Bridge."

"Then they can go back the same way," said Lady Nan Ming. She told her maids to take out a jade pot, and gave it to the young men, together with a poem describing it. She also told them that they would know the reason for her gift later. The poem read:

They come from a small boat,
And they go back via the bridge.
If you want help, tap the pot lightly,
A mandarin duck will come to your aid.

The young men bade her farewell and went

back to the bridge, escorted by one of the maids. The bridge was only several hundred paces long, with railings made in dragon patterns. As soon as they stepped on the bridge the maidservant said, with deep emotion: "As a matter of fact it was not my duty to escort you. But I have something to request of you."

Mystified, Liu Shi and Yuan Che asked, "What do you mean?"

The maidservant took a box from her sleeve; inside it there was something shaped like a spider. She gave them the box, explaining, "I am a water fairy and we don't have enough men. One year I went to Fanyu, and saw a young man. We fell in love and had a child. According to our rule, I had to abandon it, but through the kindness of Lady Nan Ming the child was adopted by the Immortal of Nanyue. Now he is three years old. Some time ago, I sent a pair of jade bracelets to him by the envoy from Huiyanfeng of Nanyue, who came to the Water Palace on business. To my consternation, he kept them for himself. So I want you two gentlemen to get them back for me."

"We would like to help you, but how can we find that envoy?" Liu Shi and Yuan Che said in chorus.

"It is not difficult to find him. When you go back to Nanyue, place this box in front of the Envoy's Temple in Huiyanfeng. You'll see what will happen."

She urged them: "Please take good care of the box, and don't open it."

The two nodded their agreement, and then asked her about the meaning of the poem which accompanied the jade pot.

The maid told them: "If you meet with any difficulty, tap the pot lightly and then fairy birds will come to your aid. In addition, the Immortal of Nanyue is your sacred guardian. You will meet him some day."

While they were talking, without realizing it, they passed the bridge and reached the place where their boat was lying. But the place looked totally different from what it had when they first arrived. They turned back to ask the maid about this change, but there was no trace of her; the bridge had vanished also.

Liu Shi and Yuan Che first went back their hometown, Hengshan, and then after a month they visited Huiyanfeng in order to keep their promise. They placed the box in the front of the Envoy's Temple as the maid had instructed. As soon as they had put it down they saw a black dragon several meters long soar from it into the sky. Then a fierce wind howled and a thunderbolt struck the temple, shattering it to pieces. Liu Shi and Yuan Che looked up at the sky in fear. But in just a few minutes the wind stopped. Just at that time they saw a pair of bracelets falling down from the sky. They took them to the Nanyue temple and put them on the altar.

When they reached their home there was a young man dressed in yellow waiting for them. He gave each of them a gold box and said:

"There is 'soul-returning extract' inside the box. When a member of your family dies you just spread the extract on the top of the dead person's head, and he or she will come back to life." Then he left.

One winter, it snowed heavily. Liu Shi and Yuan Che saw an old man selling firewood in the street outside their house. They could not bear to see the old man suffering in such clod weather and invited him inside. There they offered him hot food and wine. While they were drinking they noticed the word *taiji* on his shoulder pole. Just then they realized that he was none other than the Immortal of Nanyue. They knelt immediately and presented the jade pot.

"Oh! Finally it returns to its owner."

While saying that he took Liu Shi and Yuan Che out of the door and went towards the Zhurongfeng Peak of Mount Hengshan.

From *A Comprehensive Survey of Successive Generations of Perfected Transcendents and Those Who Embody the Tao* (Hereafter articles without sources are all from this book)

Picking up Shoes at Yiqiao Bridge

Zhang Liang was one of the founders of the Han Dynasty (206-220 B.C.). After failing to assassinate Emperor Qin Shihuang he lived in seclusion in Xiapi (present-day Suining, Jiangsu Province).

One day, while crossing the Yiqiao Bridge he saw an old man approaching. When he was close to Zhang Liang, the old man dropped his shoes over the side of the bridge. He then asked Zhang Liang to get them back for him.

Zhang Liang was nonplussed at this odd behavior, but complied with the stranger's request.

"Now you put them on," ordered the old man. Zhang Liang did so. The old man, laughing, turned to walk away, stopped and said, "You are a promising young man. Meet me here at dawn in five days' time."

At dawn on the fifth day, Zhang Liang hurried to the Yiqiao Bridge.

But he found that the old man was waiting for him already.

"Why did you come so late? Come again in

another five days." And next time be sure to be in time!" So saying, the old man went off in a huff.

The next time Zhang Liang arrived at the bridge before dawn. Unexpectedly the old man was already there again. The old man berated him, saying, "Why are you late again? Come back in another five days."

The third time Zhang Liang started waiting at the bridge the night before the fifth day. He had not been there long before the old man arrived. This time the old man was pleased. He took out a book and gave it to Zhang Liang, saying, "Master this book, you'll be an advisor to the king within ten years. You will succeed in assisting the emperor after 13 years. Then come to see me at the foot of the Mount Gucheng (in today's Dong'a, Shandong Province). You will see a yellow rock there; that will be me." Then he departed.

Zhang Liang stayed on the bridge till daybreak. He read the book, *The Art of War by Tai Gong* in the moonlight. Zhang Liang was overjoyed to have the book. From then on he shut himself up indoors and studied the book. Just as the old man had predicted, Zhang Liang's talents as a military tactician were recognized, and he did indeed rise to become the chief advisor to Liu Bang, who founded the Han Dynasty. In the 13th year of Liu Bang's reign, the two of them journeyed to Mount Gucheng, where they spotted a yellow rock. Zhang

Liang took the rock home with him and sacrificed to it all year round. When he died, the rock was buried with him.

From *Chronicles of the Han Dynasty* •
Biography of Zhang Liang

White Cranes

Su Dan was a filial son. One day, his mother suddenly thought of the salted fish sold in Zixinglong, 200 *li* away. She said that she would like to eat some, but Zixingling was too far away. Hearing this, the 14-year-old Su Dan said that he would go and buy some. Then he left. His mother thought that he had been joking, but before long Su Dan came back with a packet of salted fish and put in front of her, saying, "Here is some salted fish from Zixinglong."

His mother asked him: "How could you go to Zixinglong and back in such a short time?"

Su Dan said, "When I was in Zixinglong I saw my uncle and he sent his regards to you. He said he would be here to see you in a few days."

His mother smiled at what she still thought was a joke. She cooked the fish and tasted it; it really tasted like fish from Zixinglong. A few days later, Su Dan's uncle really did come and he said that he had met Su Dan a few days previously in Zixinglong. Astonished, Su Dan's mother questioned him closely.

Her son replied: "I've attained the Tao by

self-cultivation, and I'll ascend to Heaven and separate myself from this mortal life soon. The universe will not change my nature or limit my actions. I'll exist together with Heaven depending on my vital energy."

His mother protested, "If you leave me how can I live? Why must you leave?"

Su Dan said, "My master told me: 'if a person becomes an immortal his nine degrees of kindred will be protected. If one of them dies he or she won't change into a ghost.' Though I will be away from you I will know all about you." Then, pointing to a cabinet, he told his mother: "I leave that for you. Don't open it. If you need something, all you have to do is ask it, and I'm sure that you will get whatever you want."

Then he told his neighbors who came to see him off when they heard the news: "In two years' time there will be a pestilence in Chenzhou. You must plant orange trees everywhere and dig wells. Whoever is afflicted by this disease should eat an orange-tree leaf and drink a cup of water; then he or she will recover soon."

Just at that time, five-colored clouds gathered in the sky over the Su family's courtyard and the music of flutes and drums could be heard. Su Dan ascended the clouds, saying goodbye to his mother with tears in his eyes and bidding farewell to his neighbors with a cupped-hand salute. Then the clouds rose and floated away to the southeast.

In the third year of the reign of Emperor Wendi (177 B.C.) of the Han Dynasty, Su Dan's mother often told the cabinet what she wanted when she had difficulties. Every time, she was able to get what she needed. One day she wondered if her son was in the cabinet. So she opened it. Inside were two white cranes, which flew away immediately.

An Ordinary Person
Who Acts Like a Saint

Dongfang Shuo, a native of Yanci Township, Pingyuan County (present-day Huimin, Shandong Province), was a secretary in the government of Wuzhong (present-day Suzhou) for several decades. During the reign of Emperor Wudi of the Han Dynasty (140-87 B.C.) he submitted a petition to the emperor, written on 3,000 bamboo slips which it took two people to carry. The Emperor took two months to finish reading it. In the petition Dongfang Shuo described his own views on what the imperial court should do. Emperor Wudi was impressed by his ideas and issued an imperial edict appointing Dongfang Shuo as one of his advisors. As the Emperor trusted him, Dongfang Shou was able to get policies adopted which were of benefit to the people.

During the reign of Emperor Zhaodi (86-74 B.C.) Dongfang Shuo was considered a sage by some people and an ordinary person by others because of his unpredictable behavior. Sometimes he gave direct advice to the emperor, and sometimes used satirical means to put his ideas across. After

Xuandi ascended the throne in 73 B.C., Dongfang Shuo resigned in protest at the chaotic state of society. No one knew where he went?

Later, some people claimed to have seen him in Huiji (present-day Shaoxing) and others in the Taihu Lake area, where he was selling traditional Chinese medicine. Some knowledgeable people guessed that since Dongfang Shuo lived such a long time he must have been the spirit of the planet Jupiter.

From *Accounts of the Saints* • *Dongfang Shuo*

Dongfang Shuo Gives an Evasive Answer

During the Western Han Dynasty (206-24 B.C.), Kunming Lake was dug in the capital, Luoyang, in accordance with the wish of the emperor. At a certain depth, the soil gave way to ashes which were as black as ink. None of the civil or military officials in the imperial court knew the reason for this. So Emperor Wudi asked the knowledgeable Dongfang Shuo about it. But the latter replied:

"I'm ignorant and don't know either," he said. "You had better ask people who come from the West."

Emperor Wudi thought that if even Dongfang Shuo did not know the origin of the ashes there was no point in asking anybody else. During the reign of Emperor Mingdi (58-75) of the Eastern Han Dynasty (25-220) a Taoist priest from the West came to the capital to be presented at the court. The court officials asked the priest about the ink-black ashes. The priest said: "In the classics it says, 'when a natural disaster or universal calamity is to take place, there will be a fire disaster.' That is the sign of a fire disaster."

People then realized why Dongfang Shuo did not reveal the truth about the ashes, although he knew it.

From *Stories of Immortals*

43

A Piece of Meat and a Jar of Wine

Nobody knew where Ji Zixun came from. He was in the capital, Luoyang, during the Eastern Han Dynasty (25-220) and made a habit of calling at the mansions of the aristocracy there, with presents of one dump of meat and a single jar of wine. He would always apologize for bringing such paltry gifts, but in fact no matter how many people ate and drank all day on those occasions they could not finish the meat and wine. And when Ji Zixun took his leave there were always white clouds rising behind him, and remaining for several days. One old man said, "When I was a child I saw Ji Zixun in Huiji selling medicine in the market, and there were also white clouds behind him."

Ji Zixun did not stay long in Luoyang but went to live in seclusion in the mountains. It was said that during the Zhengshi period (240-249) of the State Wei, Ji Zixun and an old man stroked a bronze figure and then they gazed each other. Ji Zixun sighed, saying, "The bronze figure looks like it was just made a few days ago. But it is already 500 years old."

Ji Zixun and the old man walked away side by

side. It seemed that they walked slowly, but not even the swiftest steed could catch them.

From *Stories of Immortals*

Spurting Out Bees

Ge Xuan (164-244) (also known as Xiao Xian) was an alchemist of the State of Wu during the Three Kingdoms period (220-280).

One day he was dining with guests, when one guest asked him to amuse them with a magic trick.

Ge Xuan readily assented. He spurted out of his mouth the rice he had just eaten. The grains of rice immediately turned into 100 bees, which stung the guests. But the bees did not hurt them. The guests were both startled and delighted. After enjoying their consternation for a while Ge Xuan opened his mouth, and the bees flew back in. They all changed back into rice, and Ge Xuan chewed and swallowed them.

Ge Xuan had another unique skill. He could dance to the accompaniment of mysterious music with frogs, swallows or snakes. In winter he would get gifts of fresh vegetables and dates by performing this trick to entertain guests. This was not all; in summer he could produce ice and snow. Once he let people throw dozens of coins into a well. He then put a container on the edge of the well. Then he gave a call, and all the coins jumped out of the well and dropped into the container.

Another time, Ge Xuan entertained guests with wine. He poured the wine into the cups, which moved of their own accord to the individual guests. As soon as a cup was emptied it moved away automatically for a refill. Once he and Wu Zhu were sitting in an upstairs room gazing out of the window. They saw some peasants parading the street in a ceremony aimed at praying or rain. Wu Zhu turned to Ge Xuan and said,

"The peasants are suffering from drought. Would you please help them?"

Ge Xuan said, "Nothing easier!" He thereupon drew a magic figure on a piece of paper and threw it to the peasants. All of a sudden, black clouds blotted out the sky and a fierce wind howled. Rain pelted down until the street was full of water. Wu Zhu asked, "Is there any fish in the water?"

Ge Xuan drew another magic figure and threw it into the water. In only a few minutes several hundred fish appeared in the water. Wu Zhu encouraged the peasants to catch them.

Ge Xuan's magic tricks earned him the nickname "Ge the Immortal."

From *Stories of Immortals*

The Weaving Maid Helps a Mortal

A young man named Dong Yong lived in Qiancheng (present-day Qingxian in Shandong) during the Western Han period (206-24 B.C.). His mother died when Dong Yong was small. When his father too died, Dong Yong did not have enough money for the funeral. He went to a rich family and offered to work as a servant. The master of the house was moved by his filial piety, and gave him ten thousand copper coins to hold his father's funeral immediately.

After the three-year mourning period was over Dong Yong went to the rich family to work off his debt. On the way, he met a beautiful girl, who expressed her wish to marry him. After chatting for a while, they went to the rich family together.

When the master of the house saw Dong Yong he said, "I gave the money to you as a reward for your filial piety; you don't have to pay me back."

Dong Yong thanked him, but said, "Because of your kindness I managed to give my father a suitable funeral. Though I have a low social position I know that I have to pay a debt of gratitude. I beg to be allowed to work as your servant."

Then the master of the house asked, "What can the girl do?"

"She can weave," Dong Yong replied.

"If you really want to pay off the debt, why not let the girl weave 100 bolts of silk for me?" proposed the master of the house.

So they stayed there and wove day and night. In only ten days that a hundred bolt of silk were woven. Dong Yong took them to the master of the house, and then left with the girl.

Outside the door his wife told Dong Yong: "I am the Weaving Maid of Heaven. I was sent by the Heavenly Mother to help you because she was moved by your honesty and filial sentiments. Now that I have finished my task, so I have to go back."

So saying, she flew away.

From *Stories of Immortals*

The Jade Maiden Descends from Heaven

Chuan Xuanchao was an official of the Northern Prefecture of Jinan during the Jiaping reign (249-254) of the Three Kingdoms Period. One night he dreamed that a girl appeared in front of his bed. She told him that she was the Jade Maiden and came from the Eastern Prefecture. Her name was Chenggong Zhiqiong and her parents had died when she was a child. The Lord of Heaven saw that she was lonely, and so let her descend to the world and find a husband. Chuan was enthralled at how delicate and charming she was. He had the same dream for three or four successive days.

One morning, Chuan saw the Jade Maiden in real life. She was sitting in a gorgeous carriage and behind the carriage there were eight maidservants. The Jade Maiden wore embroidered silk clothes and had a delicate posture. There were wine glasses and food containers in various colors in the carriage, with rare food and fruits inside. The Jade Maiden invited Chuan Xuanchao to join her in a glass of wine. While they drank wine she told Chuan Xuanchao her story:

"I am the Jade Maiden of Heaven and was sent down to the world so that I may marry. We were together for several nights and I felt happy. So I would like to marry you. I am an immortal and can't give you a baby. But you can have another woman, and I won't be jealous."

Chuan Xuanchao was glad to have her as his wife. To praise the marriage between a mortal and a Heavenly being, the Jade Maiden wrote a long poem.

Time flew, and seven or eight years had passed before they knew it. Chuan Xuanchao took a concubine because his parents wanted to have grandsons. From then on, the Jade Maiden came to Chuan Xuanchao every other day. She was there at night and left at dawn without others being aware. Though people heard the sound of her gown rustling, they couldn't see her. This went on for a long time. Later, someone asked Chuan about this mystery, and he disclosed the secret. So Jade Maiden told Chuan that she had to leave.

The Jade Maiden said, "I don't want others to know that we are husband and wife. But since my presence has been discovered, I can't live here anymore. We have been together for many years and are deeply in love with each other. I feel sad about our separation. But I have to go, and I hope you take good care of yourself."

Then the Jade Maiden wrote a poem for him. They embraced tearfully. Then the Jade Maiden mounted the carriage and left. For a long time Chuan Xuanchao was in a low spirits.

Five years later, Chuan Xuanchao went to the capital, Luoyang, on business. He saw a carriage which was familiar to him as he passed by the foot of Mount Yushan in northern Jinan. He rushed to it and flung back the curtain. Sure enough, inside was his wife. Their reunion after such a long separation brought mixed feelings of joy and sorrow to both of them. They went to Luoyang together. They were as happy as they had been previously. It was said that they lived to the Taikang period (280-289) of the Western Jin Dynasty.

From *Stories of Immortals*

Tricking the Governor

Guo Pu (276-324) was a scholar who lived during the Jin Dynasty. Once he went to Lujiang to persuade Hu Mengkang, the governor, to leave there for the south of the Yangtze River because enemies were approaching. Governor Hu wouldn't listen to him, and as Guo Pu was preparing to leave he fell in love with a servant girl in the governor's mansion. After much hard thought as to how he could get her for his wife, he stealthily scattered red beans around the governor's mansion. The next morning the governor was astonished to see thousands of people in red clothes surrounding his house. When he went out to have a closer look, they all vanished. This happened over and over again for several days. The governor was frightened, and asked Guo Pu to exercise the strange red-clothed phantoms. Guo Pu pointed a the servant girl and said, "She is the source of this strange phenomenon. You must send here away, sir, and sell her. But do not demand a high price for her."

The governor sent the servant girl away to be sold, and Guo Pu secretly sent someone to buy her for him. Then Guo Pu drew some magic signs on a piece of paper and threw it into a well. Thereupon, the thousands of red-robed figures jumped into the well one after the other. The governor breathed a sigh of relief. Meanwhile, Guo Pu lost no time leaving Lujiang together with the girl. After ten days or so, Lujiang was occupied by enemy forces.

From *Stories of Immortals*

A General Meets His Fate

Guo Pu learned divination as a child from a Taoist priest who presented him with nine volumes of books on divination. He studied day and night until he had absorbed the knowledge contained in them by heart. The story goes that once one of Guo Pu's disciples picked up one of these books without Guo Pu's permission, and the book immediately burst into flames.

During the warfare that marked the close of the Jin Dynasty Guo Pu sought refuge in the southeast. One day he went to visit General Zhao Gu who refused to receive him because he was upset at the death of his favorite horse. Guo Pu asked the guard to tell the general that he could make the horse come back to life. Zhao Gu was overjoyed to hear that and immediately gave Guo Pu an audience. He asked his visitor what he should do to got his horse back from the dead.

Guo Pu said, "Send twenty to thirty soldiers, each with a long bamboo stick in his hand, thirty *li* east of your house to catch a strange animal which they will find in the forest."

Zhao Gu did so, and his men returned with what looked like a monkey. Guo Pu ordered the soldiers to put the animal beside the horse. When they did so the animal threw itself on the horse and sucked its mouth and nose violently. In only a few minutes, the dead horse neighed and then stood up and started to gallop around. The general was delighted, and presented Guo Pu with lavish gifts, which the latter declined, simply taking his leave.

In March of the fourth year of the Jianwu reign period (321), not long after the establishment of the Eastern Jin Dynasty (317-420), Emperor Sima Rui saw a sunspot. He summoned Guo Pu, and asked what this phenomenon portented.

Guo Pu said, "This is a sign of disaster caused by Your Majesty's abuse of his power. If Your Majesty applies a policy of benevolence, this disaster may be avoided."

The emperor was perturbed to hear this, and straightaway began to practice a policy of benevolence.

Guo Pu and Huan Yi were lifelong friends. They visited each other's houses at will. There was only one place that Guo Pu forbade his friend to enter while he himself was there, and that was the privy. In the first year of the Tianning reign period (323), Huan Yi got drunk one day in Guo Pu's house. Forgetting their agreement, stumbled to the privy, without ascertaining whether Guo Pu was there or not. Guo Pu was standing there naked, with his hair unloosed and hanging down to his shoulders. Moreover, he was holding a knife between his teeth. When he saw Huan Yi enter, he beat his breast and cried out, "Alas, disaster will come upon us both!"

During the Taining reign period (323-326) General Wang Dun planned to rebel. His assistant at the time, Guo Pu, was alarmed and tried to dissuade his master from such a rash course. One day, the general ordered Gu Pu to interpret a dream for him. Guo Pu said that the omen was not clear, but if he were cautious he would enjoy a long life; otherwise his doom awaited him round the corner. Hearing this, the general flew into a rage and ordered his guards to take Guo Pu out and execute him.

A few days, Guo Pu appeared in the street again and people talked to him. A soldier hurriedly reported this to the general, who immediately ordered that Guo Pu's coffin be opened. Sure enough, the coffin was empty. The general never recovered from the shock of this discovery, and conducted his rebellion in a trance. With such inept leadership, the revolt soon collapsed. Guo Pu's prediction proved true, as the general met death and disgrace through pursuing a reckless ambition.

From *Collected Works of Guo Hongnong*

The Death of China's First Emperor

Qin Shihuang, who unified China, become its first emperor when he founded the Qin Dynasty in 221 B.C. In the 10th year of his reign, an envoy named Zheng Rong traveled from east to west, passing Dongguan and entering Hanguguan. When he reached the boundary of Huayin he saw a mourning procession of white carriages pulled by white horses winding its way down Mount Huashan. As the lead carriage drew near, a person in it asked Zheng Rong where he was going.

"I'm going to Xianyang," Zheng Rong replied. "Good," replied the other. "I am the envoy of Death from Mount Huashan. I have a letter for the monarch of Haochi. You have to pass through Haochi on your way to Xianyang. There is a Chinese catalpa beside the road and a lump of veined marble near the tree. Strike the tree with the marble, and someone will come out to get the letter."

Zheng Rong accepted the letter and continued on his journey. When he arrived at Haochi he really did see a catalpa tree. So he knocked on it with the piece of marble. A person stepped out of the tree to get the letter. Before long, a rumor spread throughout the empire to the effect that the monarch of Haochi was about to die, and Emperor Qin Shihuang would soon follow. When this rumor reached the ears of Qin Shihuang, his health rapidly declined. The next year he died and was buried at Haochi.

From *Stories of Immortals*

The River God Demands a Wife

Zhang Pu was once the governor of Wujun Prefecture (present-day Suzhou). Nobody knew where he came from. He was relieved of his office and went back his hometown. As he passed Mount Lushan he and his family went to burn incense in Mr. Lu's Temple. One of his servant girls, pointing at a statue, said to the daughter of the governor in jest: "How about marrying him?"

The girl laughed this off, but that night Zhang's wife dreamed that Mr. Lu himself came to her and thanked her for betrothing her daughter to his son.

The next morning, Zhang's wife told her servant girls about her dream. One of them then told her about her joke of the previous day. Zhang's wife was overcome with a sense of foreboding, and urged her husband to leave that place as soon as possible. Zhang Pu acceded to her request, and the family was soon on its way again. However, just as they had forgotten all about the queer goings-on at the temple and were enjoying a ferry ride across a river, the boat suddenly stopped in midstream. Despite all the efforts of the boatman, not one inch farther could they travel.

In consternation, the passengers all threw their treasures into the river to appease the spirits of the deep. But the boat still did not move. Finally, one of them said, "It seems that the God of the River wants a wife, so we had better throw a girl into the water."

All the other people on the boat chimed their agreement with this astonishing proposal, and in the end Zhang Pu had no alternative but to agree that, as the most attractive girl on the boat, his daughter should be sacrificed. In his grief, Zhang Pu could not bear to watch his beloved daughter thrown into the river, so he turned his head away. Just as he did so, his wife pushed the sancy servant girl into the river instead. When he realized what had happened Zhang Pu flew into a rage, berating his wife and insisting that, as the boat still could make no headway, his daughter be made the River God's bride. This was done accordingly, and the boat mysteriously resumed its course.

However, as they approached the farther shore, the travelers saw both Zhang Pu's daughter and the servant girl standing there in the company of a man clad in official-looking robes. This man addressed Zhang Pu as he disembarked: "Sir, I am Mr. Lu's secretary. He instructed me to return these two girls to you, being deeply touched by your sense of duty and self-sacrifice. Besides, he acknowledges that marriage between the dead and the living is most improper.

The travellers eagerly questionned the girls about the world at the bottom of the river. But all they said was that they had seen palaces, officials and soldiers there; they had had no sense of being under water at all.

From *Stories of Immortals*

Not a Sideway Glance

Mi Zhu, a native of Juxian County, Donghai (present-day Lianyungang, Jiangsu Province), was the brother-in-law of Liu Bei (161-223) founder of the State of Shu Han (221-263). He engaged in trade, and often travelled to the capital Luoyang on business.

Once he was on the way back home from Luoyang when he saw a woman standing beside the road. She was pretty and was dressed like a bride. She asked him for a lift in his cart. Mi Zhu agreed, but while they were seated side by side Mi Zhu did not even look at her sideways. After about 20 *li* the woman asked to dismount. Before leaving she told Mi Zhu:

"I am a servant of the Lord of Heaven. I was ordered to burn down your house in Donghai. But I was moved by your honesty, so I wanted to tell you the truth."

Mi Zhu was amazed to hear this and begged her to spare his house. But the woman said, "It is God's will. I can't disobey it. But you hurry home ahead of me. I will follow slowly, but some time after noon your house will burn to the ground."

Mi Zhu rushed home and evacuated all his family and their belongings. Sure enough, that afternoon their house was destroyed by fire.

From *Stories of Immortals*

The Magic Swords

During the Warring States period (475-221 B.C.), in the State of Chu there lived a man named Gan Jiang and his wife Mo Xie. They were both skilled armorers. Once they were ordered to cast a pair of swords, one male and the other female, for the King of Chu. The task took three years to complete.

On the day he was to take the swords to the king, Gan Jiang said to Mo Xie, who was about to give birth: "The king is sure to be angry at the delay, and will have me killed. I am only going to give the king the female sword; the other I will hide beneath a rock upon which a pine is growing on Mount Nanshan. If the child is a boy, tell him to avenge me with that sword."

When the king of Chu, already annoyed at the time taken to make the swords, found out that Gan Jiang had only brought one sword he had him executed on the spot. Mo Xie gave birth to a boy not long after that. He was named Chi Bi. After more than a dozen years the boy grew into a strapping young man. One day he asked his mother: "Mother, where is my father?"

Mo Xie said sadly: "Your father was executed by the king because he took three years to cast swords for him. The king thought that was too slow. Your father told me that the male sword is hidden beneath a rock on which a pine tree grows, on Mount Nanshan, south of our house. He said that you should use that sword to avenge him."

Then, Chi Bi went out of the house and journeyed to the south. He found the large rock under a pine tree on Mount Nanshan. He split the rock with an axe and found the sword and set off to avenge his father. Meanwhile the king of Chu was haunted by nightmares. He dreamed that a young man with a sword in his hand, was looking for him, shouted that he would avenge his father. The king offered a thousand pieces of gold for the capture of the young man. Hearing that there was a price on his head, Chi Bi took refuge in the mountains. There he met a magician, who took pity on his plight and offered to help him avenge his father. "Give me your head and your sword," he said , "and I will ensure that your illustrious father lies easy in his grave."

Chi Bi readily agreed. Drawing his sword, he cut his own head off.

The magician took the head and sword to the king of Chu. He advised the king to have the head boiled to remove its enmity. The king did so, but after three days the head was still intact. In fact, it even jumped out of the pot and glanced at the king with blazing eyes.

The magician thereupon told the king that only when the boiling head was watched by the king himself would its venom disappear. So the king ordered that the head be put back in the pot. As he approached the pot himself, the magician cut his head off with the magic sword. He then cut his own head off, and so there were three heads boiling in the pot.

From *Stories of Immortals*

The Maiden and the God

When Wu Wangzi, a country girl, was about 16 years old she went to a temple fair. As she was walking by a stream on her way there she saw a high-ranking official sitting in a boat. When he saw Wu Wangzi he ordered his men to ask her where she was going.

Wu Wangzi told him her destination, and the official invited her to join him in the boat because he was going to the same place.

Wu Wangzi was shy, and declined. All of a sudden, the boat and the official disappeared. Wangzi realized that she had met a god. So she cupped her hands and raised them in the air as a gesture of courtesy, closing her eyes as she did so. When she opened her eyes she saw the official sitting in front of her. It turned out to be a statue of the god Jiang Hou. The statue spoke to her and gave her two oranges.

From then on, Jiang Hou and Wangzi made contact constantly, and a deep affection developed between them. Anything Wangzi thought of would fall from the sky. If she wanted to eat fish a fresh carp would come to her. As people got to know about this, they asked her to do favors for them. She granted whatever was requested.

From *Stories of Immortals*

The Lovesick Trees

Han Ping was one of the secretaries of King Kang (?-286 B.C.) of the State of Song, who was an unprincipled, dim-witted ruler. The king seized Han Ping's wife and imprisoned Han Ping. The latter committed suicide. Not long afterwards, as the king and his retinue were disporting themselves on a high terrace Han Ping's wife suddenly threw herself over the edge. The king's attendants rushed to stop her, but were too late. They were left holding her jacket. In one of the pockets they found a note expressing her wish to be buried with her husband.

But such was the vicious mind of the king that he ordered the couple to be buried separately.

The next day, a catalpa tree started growing out of each tomb. The two trees eventually twined together and two birds made their nest there. They stay in the trees day and night chirping sadly. The people of Song mourned for Han Ping and his wife, and named the catalpa trees the "lovesick trees" and the birds the "lovesick birds." Some people said the birds were the spirits of Han Ping and his wife. In memory of the couple today there is a city called Hanping City in Suiyang, Shangqiu County, Henan

Province. The story is still told among the local people.

From *Stories of Immortals*

A Cup of Wine Separated by a Hairpin

Zuo Ci, a famous Taoist magician during the Three Kingdoms period (220-280), was noted for being able to multiply himself into as many bodies as he wanted. He once made sarcastic remarks about Cao Cao, the prime minister, who flew into a rage and put him in prison. But while one Zuo Ci languished behind bars, another went about his everyday business.

Once Cao Cao invited Zuo Ci to a banquet. The guest poured a cup of wine and divided the wine into two with his hairpin. Then he drank half the wine and offered the other half to Cao Cao. When Cao Cao refused to drink, Zuo Ci drank the other half too. Then he threw the cup into the rafters, where it turned into a bird. Zuo Ci thereupon vanished.

Incensed, Cao Cao ordered that Zuo Ci be found and executed. To make sure that they got the right Zuo Ci, the soldiers were told to slay every man missing a left eye, as Zuo Ci's left eye was missing. No sooner had this order been issued than such people mysteriously appeared all over the city.

The soldiers thereupon chopped the heads off all of them and took them to Cao Cao. But when Cao Cao examined the heads he found that they were made of cogongrass.

Zuo Ci next went to Jingzhou, where the prefect, Liu Biao, was holding a military review. He told the prefect that he wished to treat his soldiers to wine and meat. Liu Biao scoffed when he saw that Zuo Ci was carrying with him only one jar of wine and one lump of dried meat. But when Zuo Ci handed the wine and meat to Liu Biao's attendants, even ten of them could not lift the gifts. Zuo Ci then started to distribute cups of wine and pieces of meat. Miraculously every man in this huge army received one piece of meat and three cups of wine!

Bidding farewell to Liu Biao, Zuo Ci went visit another Taoist, Xu Zhui, who lived in Dongwu, south of the Yangtze River. The gatekeeper of Xu Zhui's house, not knowing who Zuo Ci was, and unimpressed by the one-eyed man's shabby appearance, refused to admit him.

Zuo Ci, thereupon made the oxen which were tethered outside the gate suddenly appear on the treetops. At the same time, the wheels of the farm carts sprouted sharp thorns. The gatekeeper, in a panic reported this to Xu Zhui, who immediately guessed who his visitor was. He sent the man to apologize to Zuo Ci, who then restored the oxen and carts to their original condition.

Zuo Ci's uncanny powers earned him many

enemies. One of them was the general Sun Ce. The general, on the pretext of hospitality, took Zuo Ci on an outing, plotting to kill him by running him through with a spear from behind. But although he was seated astride his swiftest horse there was no way that he could catchup with Zuo Ci, who was plodding along on foot ahead of him.

Eventually Zuo Ci retired to Mount Huoshan, where he devoted himself to making pills of immortality, in the end becoming an immortal himself.

From *The History of the Later Han Dynasty* • *Biography of Zuo Ci*

Warning the Monkeys off the Millet

Jie Xiang, a native of Huiji (present-day Shaoxing, Zhejiang Province), was a wise man of the State of Wu (222-280) in the Three Kingdoms period. He read all the Five Classics (*The Book of Songs, The Book of History, The Book of Changes, The Book of Rites* and *The Spring and Autumn Annals*) and studied various schools of thought and their exponents during the period from pre-Qin times to the early years of the Han Dynasty.

Jie Xiang went into the mountains to find a teacher of the Tao. But even after several months he failed to find one.

One day he found himself in a valley which was blocked at one end. Suddenly a beautiful girl appeared before him. He realized that she was no ordinary person, and so he kowtowed to her.

The girl told him to go home and refrain from eating meat for three years, and then to return.

Jie Xiang did so, and sure enough after three years the girl was really waiting for him. She then gave him a book on how to become an immortal.

Jie Xiang devoted himself to studying the book. Later on, when he was staying in Le Yanya's home, he used to frequent a grove where other scholars often gathered. These scholars were so impressed by Jie Xiang's scholarship that they recommended him to the king of Wu as an advisor. After some hesitation, he finally accepted the king's offer.

Jie Xiang, despite his exalted position, was always willing to help humble people.

One day a peasant complained that his millet field was constantly being raided by monkeys. Jie Xiang said, "Don't worry. When the monkeys come tomorrow, you just tell them that you have told Mr. Jie about their antics. Say that he orders them to keep away from the millet field." The peasant did so, and, sure enough, had no more trouble from the monkeys.

From *Records of Immortals*

To Cure the Sickness, First Improve the Patient's Morals

At the end of the Sui (581-618) and beginning of the Tang (618-907) dynasties, there was a famous doctor named Sun Simiao. The *Precious Prescriptions* and *Supplement to Precious Prescriptions* written by him are the classics of traditional Chinese medicine (TCM) as well as required reading for all TCM doctors. In his childhood, Sun was very clever. At the age of seven, he could recite lengthy passages from Lao Zi and Zhuang Zi as well as TCM books. Hence his neighbors called him a child prodigy. Due to upheavals and wars, Sun withdrew from society and retired to Mount Taibai (now Mount Tiantong in the east of Yinxian County in Zhejiang Province), where he devoted all his time to studying Taoist doctrines. After a few years he became an expert in astronomy, geography, the theory of *yin* and *yang* and TCM. One day while out walking, Sun saw a boy beating a small green snake, which was bleeding. Having pity on the snake, Sun offered his coat to the boy if he would stop beating the snake. The boy did so, and Sun healed the snake of its wounds and then set it free.

One month later Sun descended the mountain on a journey. Reaching the road at the foot of the mountain, he saw a young man in a white robe holding a horse by the bridle and standing by the roadside with a crowd of servants. Seeing Sun, they quickly came up to greet him.

The young man said, "Your humble younger brother has waited for you for quite a long time." Thereupon, a servant invited Sun to mount the horse. He was then escorted to a city, which had wide streets lined with flowers and trees, and magnificent houses. The people there were well-dressed and cultured. Soon they came to a house with high walls. The young man in the white robe led Sun inside, and into a hall, where an elegant and poised lady accompanied by a group of maids in purple clothes approached and saluted him, with "the benefactor has come. It was remiss of me not to come out to greet you. A few days ago when my son went out by himself, he was beaten by a foolish boy. Fortunately you saved him. So I have invited you here today to express our gratitude to you."

So saying, the lady waved her hand, and a young man in a green robe emerged from an inner chamber. Seeing Sun, he hurriedly fell to his knees. Sun suddenly realized that the lady's son was none other than the green snake that he had saved. He was informed that the lady was a divinity, and that the mansion he had been brought to was the Palace of the Jingyang River.

The lady had lanterns lit and a banquet set for Sun. In the twinkling of an eye, a table was covered by delicious food and wine, while girls danced to the accompaniment of an orchestra. However, Sun demurred: "As a Taoist, I am not interested in worldly things like banquets."

Then the lady told the maids to present Sun with various rare treasures, but Sun declined with a wave of his hand. The lady then presented him with the *Secret Classic of the Dragon Palace*, which had been handed down from ancient times. She said, "This is a medical book and will help you cure people. It is a Taoist treasure."

Sun accepted the gift and thanked the lady. Soon afterwards, he took his leave, and went to practice medicine in the city. Whenever he met with difficult and complicated cases, he would refer to the prescriptions written in the book. All of the prescriptions worked well, and Simiao enjoyed a high reputation.

In the early days of the Tang Dynasty a talented poet named Lu Zhaolin (about 635-689) lived in Fanyang (in present-day Zhuoxian County, Hebei Province). He was one of the four famous poets of the early Tang. Falling ill, he consulted Sun Simiao on his theory of healing.

Sun replied, "I have learnt that one who knows well the ways of Heaven must know human affairs well too. There are four seasons — spring, summer, autumn and winter. Cold and hot air come alternately. The mixture of cold and hot air produces

79

rain; the conflict between cold and hot air gives birth to wind; the condensation of cold and hot air results in frost or snow. This is a natural law that cannot be reversed. Each person has the four limbs (arms and legs) and the five internal organs (heart, liver, spleen, lungs and kidneys). A person works during the daytime and sleeps at night, and has to inhale oxygen and exhale carbon dioxide. If every internal organ works well, the person will be in good health. This is also the natural law for human beings. The combination of *yin* with *yang*, and men with women is normal. Too much *yang* will produce internal heat; and too much *yin* will give birth to warts, which will gradually turn into subcutaneous ulcers. If a person suffering from subcutaneous ulcers engages in work, he or she will gasp for breath and become thin and pallid.

"Hence the fact that a person is sick is just as if day and night were mixed up, there was an imbalance among the stars, the sun and moon turned in a wrong way, and the comets flew away freely. All these phenomena prove that the nature is sick. If the climate does not become cold when it should, or vice versa, it means that nature suffers from a heat disease; if there appear earthquakes and landslides, it means the earth suffers from pain; and if there is a violent storm, it means the earth gasps for breath. If there is a flood or drought, it means the earth has become thin and pallid. A good doctor can save patients with medicines and cure them with good prescriptions, but the doctor himself must have good medical morals. Natural disasters can be eliminated, and people's diseases too can be prevented and cured."

Upon hearing Sun's words, Lu Zhaolin asked:

"What kind of person should I be?"

Sun said: "A person should act like a man of noble character. When meeting difficulties, he or she should have courage and insight, as well as the determination to make a prompt decision. In this way, he or she will not be afraid of any difficulty."

"What is the key to keeping in good health?" Zhaolin asked again.

Sun replied, "Sometimes nature becomes weak, and so will human beings. If a person does not cultivate his physical and mental capabilities, he will not keep fit. So people should be very careful about their words and acts. If a learned person does not pay attention to his words and acts, he will not have love and justice. For instance, peasants without moral integrity do not grow crops well; and merchants without morals do not do business well. A son without morals does not show filial obedience to his parents; an elder without morals is not kind; officials without morals can not make great contributions; and if a ruler of a country does not have morals, the country under his rule will be in great disorder."

From *History of the Tang Dynasty* •
Biography of Sun Simiao

Emperor Xuanzong
Bumps into a Wall

Wu Daozi (685-?) was one of the renowned painters of the Tang Dynasty. He excelled at painting figures and landscapes, especially Buddhist and Taoist figures. He created more than 300 murals, his skill reaching the acme of perfection. Later Wu Daozi became an immortal, and was known as Daoyuan.

In the early days of his reign, Emperor Xuanzong of the Tang exerted himself to make the country prosperous. But later in his reign he grew tired of politics, and became corrupt and incompetent, thus bringing great disorder to the country. One day, the emperor, who had heard of Wu Daozi for quite a long time, summoned him to the palace and, pointing to a blank wall, ordered him to paint anything he liked on it.

Daozi asked for a few white cloth curtains, and had them hung on the wall. Then a bucket of Chinese ink was prepared. Daozi raised the white cotton curtains one by one with one hand, and systematically splashed the ink onto the wall with the other. He lift the curtains covering the wall.

When the emperor asked him what he had painted, Wu Daozi answered, "Mountains, rivers, figures, etc. Your Majesty may have a look now."

The curtains were taken away, showing a beautiful landscape painting with peaks rising one higher than another, streams running swiftly, tall trees, figures, cottages, and rare animals and birds. Surprisingly the trees in the painting were swaying gently in the breeze; and smoke was coming from the cottages. After gazing at the painting with great appreciation, Xuanzong said, with deep feeling: "There are a large number of painters in the imperial palace, but none of them is as accomplished as you."

Wu Daozi walked slowly to the wall and, pointing at a valley in the painting, said, "Your Majesty, there is a cave under the rocks. In the cave lives an immortal. Why don't you go and knock on his door and see if there is anyone inside?"

Xuanzong, doubtful, knocked on the door. The door opened, and a fairy messenger boy came out and stood just outside.

Wu Daozi then said to Xuanzong: "The scenery in the cave is extremely beautiful. Let me go inside first, and you follow behind."

So saying, the painter jumped into the painting and beckoned to Xuanzong to follow him into the cave. But when the emperor tried to do so, he bumped into the wall. At this moment, Wu Daozi turned his head, smiled and entered the cave. As soon as he had stepped inside, the door of the cave closed behind him.

Xuanzong stood there stunned, until an imperial guard ran in to report:

"Your Majesty, Wu Daozi has left the Forbidden City, riding a donkey."

Xuanzong flew into rage. When he turned around to look at the painting again, all he saw was a blank wall.

From *Miscellanies of Emperor Xuanzong of the Tang Dynasty*

Grandpa Helps His
Grandson's Servant

Xu Xuanping, a native of Shexian County, Xin'an Prefecture, lived in seclusion at Nanwu on Mount Chengyang during the reign of the Tang Dynasty Emperor Ruizong (710-711). His thatched cottage was simple, but very clean and tidy. While engaging in self-cultivation, Xu Xuanping ate only simple food, and sometimes did not eat anything. At the age of over 70, he looked like a vigorous man of 40. He could walk as fast as a galloping horse. He often cut firewood and sold it in the market, or picked medicinal herbs and gave them to others. On his carrying pole there was always a gourd ladle and a bamboo stick. He loved to drink wine, and often got drunk.

Xu Xuanping had a facile imagination, and especially excelled at writing poems in his own unique style. When going out with firewood on his shoulder, he often chanted his *Firewood Song* as follows:

> *In the morning I carry firewood to sell it;*
> *And I return home when the sun is setting.*

If you ask me where my home is,
It is amidst crape myrtles in the clouds.

As a good doctor of traditional Chinese medicine, Xu Xuanping offered free treatment and free medicine to all his patients. Hence he enjoyed a high reputation among the local people. However, during the reign of Tianbao period (742-756) of Emperor Xuanzong, he often left home to go on journeys. People who paid visits to his cottage at those times used to find a poem pasted outside, which read:

I have lived in seclusion for 30 years;
In my cottage built on the mountaintop.
I often enjoy the bright moon at night,
And drink clean spring water during the day.
As a woodcutter, I often sing in the mountains,
While birds flit around the rocks.
I am so happy that I forget my age,
Although I am over 60.

This poem spread like wildfire. Even people in Chang'an, Luoyang, Tongxiang and Hangzhou cities got to know it, as it was copied and pasted up in many places frequented by travelers.

Also during the Tianbao reign period, Li Bai (701-762), a famous poet, offended some influential officials and had to resign his position as a Hanlin academician. He left Chang'an to go eastward and put up at an inn for the night, where he found the poem on the wall. Having read it time and time again, Li Bai sighed: "It is a poem written by an immortal." Wanting to meet Xu Xuanping, Li Bai sought him out at his cottage. Xu was not at home, so Li Bai left a poem for him, which read:

> I read your poem at an inn,
> Then I came to pay you a visit.
> I couldn't find your footprints in the misty
>   mountains,
> As there were clouds and forests between you
>   and me.
> I found your courtyard bleak and chilly,
> Leaning on a stick, I was at a loss what to do.
> I wish I could be a crane
> And come to see you again in a thousand years.

After reading Li Bai's poem, Xu Xuanping straightaway wrote a reply:

> My clothes are patched-up lotus leaves,
> Crops from a tiny field are enough for me.
> As others continually pester me
> I have to seek a more secluded life.

After that Xuanping never returned to his thatched cottage.

In Xiantong reign period (860-873) of Emperor Yizong of the Tang Dynasty, Xu Xuanping was over 100 years old and unknown to the young people. In the 12th year of Xiantong reign, Xu Mingshu, a descendant of the Xu family, had a maid servant. She was very diligent. She did all the housework, and often went deep into the mountains to cut firewood by herself. However, her master failed to appreciate her services. One day, on her way to cut firewood, she saw an old man sitting on a rock. Upon seeing the maid servant, the old man asked, "Do you work for Xu Mingshu?"

"Yes," the maid answered shyly.

"I'm an ancestor of your master. Is that a surprise to you?"

The maid was very glad to hear it. She hastily kneeled down on the ground and said, "I often hear my master mention you. He said that you attained perfection in Taoism. He has not seen you for dozens of years. Will you allow me to take you to him?"

"That is unnecessary." Xu Xuanping said. "Could you please tell Mingshu that I am here and am well. Don't let anyone come to the mountains to look for me. It is unsafe in the mountains because there are tigers and wolves here."

The maid agreed.

"You work very hard for Mingshu's family, but they are unfair to you. Don't feel wronged; you will be fairly rewarded in the future," the old man said.

"I have my own fate. I must work hard and not be upset by criticism. How can I have a grudge against my master? Please don't worry about that."

"You are very reasonable and kind. You never bear grudges against others. How praiseworthy!"

He then offered her a peach. But the girl, remembering that the old man had been about to eat it when she had come across him, refused. Xu Xuanping insisted that she eat the peach, and then sent her home.

When she reported this encounter to her master, he was angry with her for not bringing his ancestor to him. But as soon as his rod touched the maid servant's back she flew up into the sky. Later, it was said that she had been seen in the mountains with Xu Xuanping.

Li Bai and Bai Guinian

Li Bai and Bai Guinian were literary figures who lived in different eras, but there is a legend that they once met.

One of the greatest poets of the era, Li Bai, was forced into exile by this upheaval. In the 11th month of the first year of the Baoying reign period (762) he drowned while admiring the reflection of the moon in a pond after drinking heavily.

The poet was said to have studied Taoism, and after his death he was reported to have been seen several times chatting with Taoist hermits in the mountains.

A hundred years later, Bai Guinian, a descendant of the Tang poet Bai Juyi, took a trip to Mount Songshan. He climbed the mountain and viewed the ancient tall trees in the distance. Suddenly a boy appeared, and said, "Hanlin Academician Li summons you." Following the boy, Bai Guinian came to an open space in the misty forest full of rare flowers. In the middle there was a stone table and some stone benches. By the table sat an old man in a white robe and with rosy cheeks and beautiful snow-white hair. Seeing Guinian, the old man stood up and greeted him with a smile:

"I am Li Bai. Are you Bai Guinian, a descendant of Bai Juyi?"

Bai Guinian, astonished, went forward to salute him. Li Bai explained, "I have held a post here for over 100 years. All edicts from the Heavenly Emperor and memorials to him are handled here. Not long ago, when I was crossing Tongguan Pass, I met your ancestor, and gave him a poem I had written."

Li Bai then recited it:

I once visited the Peach Blossom Cave,
Where I heard lovely songs and saw elegant
*   dances.*
I am often reminded of the beautiful scene:
The bright moon, fallen flowers and mist.
Just like a tearful dream in which I saw my
*   friend off.*

"Where is my ancestor now?" Guinian asked.

"He is on Mount Wutai, where he is in charge of all merits and virtues on earth. His dream of being an upright man has come true." So saying, Li Bai took out a book and gave it to Bai Guinian.

"Go back to read this book. Then you will be able to distinguish truth from falsehood, understand birds' and animals' languages and cultivate your merits and virtues."

Guinian took the book home and studied it. A

few years later he was able to understand birds' and animals' languages. Later when someone asked him where Li Bai was, he answered that Li Bai was a true man of the superior heaven, and Bai Juyi, the master of the Penglai Fairyland.

The Floating Mat

Zhang Zhihe, styled Xianzhenzi, was a native of Yinshan in Huiji (present-day Shaoxing, Zhejiang Province). A learned scholar, he was fond of wine, and had a legendary capacity for drinking. Moreover he was accomplished at *qigong*: He could lie in the snow and not feel cold, and could fall into water and emerge completely dry. In his youth, he liked roaming around, and visited all the famous sights in China.

Zhang Zhihe had a bosom friend, Yan Zhenqing (709-785), a famous calligrapher. Thanks to his merits earned in the suppression of the An Lushan-Shi Siming Rebellion, Yan was later promoted to Minister of Personnel. When serving as inspector of Huzhou Prefecture, he often drank wine with Zhang Zhihe. On such occasions he would sing the *Fishermen's Song*, which Zhang had written:

> *Egrets are flying around Mount Xisai,*
> *Where there are peach blossoms, tinkling streams and big mandarin fish.*
> *With a green bamboo hat and a straw rain cape,*

I needn't go back despite blustery weather.

Together with Lu Hongjian, Xu Shiheng, Li Chengju and others, Yan Zhenqing wrote 25 folk songs.

Zhang Zhihe also excelled at painting flowers, trees, birds, fish, landscapes and fantastic scenery.

One day during a trip to Pingwang, Yan Zhenqing ran into Zhang Zhihe. They were so happy that they decided to drink their fill. Zhang Zhihe laid a mat on a stream. The two of them sat on the mat, drinking wine. The mat floated to and fro, like a boat. Now the mat went swiftly, and now slowly. Around the mat there flew some cranes. Yan Zhenqing was overjoyed and didn't return until he had enjoyed himself to the full.

From *Sequel to Accounts of the Saints · Xuan Zhenzi*

Music of the Rainbow and Feather Clothes and *the Heavenly Master Canal*

Emperor Xuanzong of the Tang Dynasty once took a tour of the moon palace with a Taoist named Fashan (616-720). It was he who helped the emperor compose the *Music of the Rainbow and Feather Clothes*.

Originally, Emperor Gaozong (reigned 653-683), grandfather of Emperor Xuanzong, had offered Fashan an official post. But Fashan declined and retired to his study. Emperor Gaozong was keen on practicing Taoism and making pills of immortality. He gathered alchemists from all over the country to make pills of immortality out of gold. All of them failed. Seeing this, Fashan petitioned the emperor to get rid of the achemists, as they were charlatans and were wasting vast amounts of resources. Emperor Gaozong accepted his advice.

In the Guanghan Palace, on the moon, mythical birds and phoenixes sang and danced to the accompaniment of melodious music. Xuanzong asked Fashan: "What is the name of that tune?"

"It is heavenly music called *Purple Cloud*

Music for the dance performed by mythical birds and phoenixes. You looked attentively at the dance, but did not listen to the music carefully."

Emperor Xuanzong then learned the tune by heart.

The handle of the Big Dipper moved, and the emperor and Fashan left the Guanghan Palace for the earth. On their way back, they looked down at Luzhou Prefecture. In the dead of night all was quiet. Fashan took out a jade flute and gave it to the emperor. Then the emperor began to play the *Purple Cloud Music*. While listening to the music, Fashan threw coins down onto the prefecture.

The following day, Emperor Xuanzong, who still had the heavenly music in his head, bent over his desk to write it down. Then he gathered all the court singers and dancers to rehearse the *Purple Cloud Dance*. Created on the basis of the dance performed by fairy maidens on the moon and the Rainbow Lady, it was named the *Music of the Rainbow and Feather Clothes*. The music soon spread far and wide. Later, Bai Juyi, a famous poet, specially recorded the structure of the music and the scene of a performance.

On the 10th day after the pair had returned to Earth, the prefect of Luzhou Prefecture submitted a memorial to the throne, saying that at the Mid-Autumn Festival, music had been heard in the sky, and coins had fallen to the ground. Reading the memorial, the emperor and Fashan smiled knowingly. Then the emperor issued an edict, saying that the coins should be used for the people of Luzhou Prefecture.

Soon afterwards, Fashan went to reside at Siming Terrace, a Taoist Temple. On the first day of the fifth lunar month an old man appeared, weeping and asking Fashan to help him accomplish charitable and pious deeds.

"What difficulty have you?" Fashan said.

The old man said, "I am the dragon of the East China Sea. The Heavenly Emperor ordered me to guard the treasures of the eight seas. If I don't make any mistake during the 1,000 years when I am on duty, I will become a celestial. Until now I have done the job without any mistake for 970 years. To my surprise, a Buddhist magician disciple, who tries to show off his power, has come to the seashore, reciting an incantation: To the effect that on the fifth day of the fifth lunar month the sea will dry up. So I have come here to ask you for help."

"What can I do for you?" Fashan said.

"I want you to draw a talisman for me and throw it into the sea to prevent the sea from drying up. Then ask him to hand the treasure he has stolen to you. You needn't kill him."

Fashan did as he was asked. Seeing Fashan, the Buddhist realized that Fashan has stronger supernatural power than he. Ashamed, he killed himself. On the next day, the old man came to express his gratitude to Fashan with a cartload of treasures. ˉ

"I live in wild mountains; pearls and other treasures are useless to me. Take them back to the Dragon Palace," said Fashan.

The old man was at a loss how to thank Fashan, until he suddenly hit upon an idea: There are no springs in the mountains. Why don't I channel water for both Fashan and the local people.

Fashan thought that this was an excellent idea, and that night when the moon had just come up, there was a huge landslide, which opened up a ditch, along which water in abundance flowed. The ditch, named the "Heavenly Master Ditch," still exists today.

From *New History of the Tang Dynasty* •
Stories About Alchemists and
Miscellanies of Emperor Xuanzong

Luo Gongyuan Teases Emperor Xuanzong

Luo Gongyuan, also known as Luo Siyuan, Luo Gongda and Immortal Luo, was a native of Jiulong County, Pengzhou Prefecture (present-day Pengzhou City, Sichuan Province). Legend has it that he became an immortal during the Xianhe reign period (326-334) of Emperor Chengdi of the Jin Dynasty. For several hundred years in the Sui and Tang dynasties he lived in Luochuan and Liyuan. In the third month of the first year of the Kaiyuan reign period of the Tang Dynasty, he arrived in Ezhou Prefecture (present-day Wuchang, Hubei Province).

One day the prefect of Ezhou threw a banquet in a garden, which attracted a large number of local gentlemen and celebrities. At the height of the banquet, a tall and dignified young man calmly approached the entrance of the garden, his white robe flapping in the breeze. The gatekeeper, who had never seen him before, stopped him, for he had no invitation card. Suddenly a boy came and shouted, "Who let you leave your post to come here? Go back to your post right now."

Turning his head and seeing the boy, the young man left without saying a word. The boy explained to the prefect: "My name is Luo Gongyuan. I saw the river-guarding dragon leaving his post, so I followed him here."

When the prefect expressed incredulity, the boy said, "If you and your guests wish to see the dragon, then come to the river bank by the Jin Pavilion the day after tomorrow." With that, he ran away. Overcame by curiosity, the prefect and his guests gathered at the spot at the appointed time. Before long, the boy appeared from the middle of the river and mounted the bank. There he squatted down and scratched a small ditch in the soil, into which he poured water from the river. He showed the onlookers a tiny white fish which was swimming in the ditch. Before their very eyes, the fish leaped out of the ditch and made straight for the river. As it did so, a misty rain began to fall. Everyone ran for the shelter of the pavilion. There they were enveloped in a fog so thick that they could not even see each other. This was followed by a violent thunderstorm, which whipped up surging waves on the river. After half an hour the weather cleared up, and a white dragon was seen to soar from the river into the sky.

The prefect was so impressed by this that he took the boy into his service. It was then that the boy revealed himself as Luo Gongyuan, who had taken on such a disguise.

Later, Luo Gongyuan was summoned by Emperor Xuanzong to join the eminent Taoists Zhang Guolao and Ye Fashan at his palace.

After having entered the palace, Luo Gongyuan got along well with Zhang Guolao and Ye Fashan, but not with the emperor.

Rishuzi was a kind of fruit peculiar to Jiannan, Sichuan Province. One day Emperor Xuanzong, Zhang Guolao and Ye Fashan tried to obtain *rishuzi* with magic powers. All day they waited, but no *rishuzi* appeared. Finally, Luo Gongyuan walked into the room and pulled an iron attachment from the stove. Immediately, a heavenly messenger appeared with the *rishuzi* they had been waiting for. Ya Fashan asked him why he was late. The other replied that the city was in flames when he arrived, and only when the fire had died down was he able to enter.

This was one of the many occasions on which Luo Gongyuan proved himself superior to the emperor's favorite magicians.

One day Emperor Xuanzong asked Luo Gongyuan to teach him magic powers. But Lu Gongyuan said, "Your Majesty should follow the examples of the sage kings Yao and Shun, and govern the country by doing nothing. You should also carry on the tradition of frugality started during the reign of Emperor Wen and Emperor Jing (179-139 B.C.) of the Han Dynasty. How can you neglect the affairs of state and let your ancestors and the country down simply to learn insignificant tricks. If you really want to learn my magic powers, you must first go deep into the people to unite and love them. Have you ever seen a Taoist with an imperial jade seal on his breast?"

Luo Gongyuan then started to enumerate the emperor's faults. Emperor Xuanzong flew into rage. He pulled out his sword and slashed at his tormentor. When Gongyuan hid himself in a flagpole, the emperor split the pole; when Gongyuan hid in a pillar, the emperor cut the pillar to pieces. However, each piece had Gongyuan's shadow. Seeing this, Emperor Xuanzong changed his tactics. He bowed to Gongyuan, and begged his forgiveness.

Gongyuan taught the emperor how to make himself invisible. The emperor tried the magic several times in the presence of Gongyuan, and it worked well. But when he practiced it by himself, it did not work satisfactorily, leaving his belt or underwear visible. The emperor blamed Gongyuan for not teaching him properly. Perceiving a threat to his life, Gongyuan fled into exile.

A few years later, an imperial envoy named Xian Yu met Gongyuan by chance in Sichuan Province. Gongyuan told him: "I came to Sichuan during the Xianhe reign period of Emperor Cheng of the Jin Dynasty. I lived in the forest and concentrated on practicing Taoism. Later I learnt that the emperor loved Taoism. So I left the forest and came back to the ordinary world, trying to cultivate the emperor with Taoism and benefit the people. However, the emperor put me to work making pills of immortality for him and teaching him magic powers. I told him it would take him 10 years to become an immortal, but he was impatient. Moreover he even tried to kill me. He is such a tyrant. Originally I planned to punish him, but now I have changed my mind because I think we all belong to Heaven."

So saying, Luo Gongyuan took a letter from his sleeve and handed it to Xian Yu. "Please give this letter to him. In the letter I tell him I, Luo Gongyuan, am disciple of Mr. Qingzheng. I hope he will understand something after having read it. Otherwise he has only himself to blame."

Xian Yu accepted the letter, and Gongyuan flew away on a cloud.

Ruling the State by
Keeping to the "One"

One day in the ninth month of the fourth year (939) of the Tianfu reign period of the Jin Dynasty, Emperor Gaozu asked the Taoist Zhang Jianming: "May I administer the country with Taoist philosophy?"

"Yes," Zhang Jianming said. "Tao, or the Way, is the basic principle of the universe. Taoists with morals should start from observing *yin* and *yang*. A person who grasps the meaning of Tao follows the doctrine of *wu-wei*, or "doing nothing," and observes movement while staying still. He knows everything in the world without even leaving home; and knows the natural law without even looking out of the window. Moreover, he can administer the country in this way."

Upon hearing this, the emperor invited Zhang Jianming to stay in the inner palace and be his teacher.

One day, when Zhang Jianming was having a chat with the emperor, he suddenly heard the sound of a drum sounding the hour. He said to Gaozu: "Your Majesty, listen to the sound of the drum? Its basic beat is 'one.' 'One' is the foundation of sound. The five notes of the Chinese five-tone scale and the 12 temperaments all originate from 'one.' Hence 'one' is the source of all things on earth. So by keeping the 'one' you may administer your country." Emperor Gaozu nodded in agreement.

Brocade Bees and Butterflies

During the Qingli reign period (1041-1048) of Emperor Renzong of the Song Dynasty, a man named Zhang Jiuge, who was reputed to have magic powers, lived in the capital.

One day Prince Yan asked Zhang Jiuge: "Do you know Taoist magic?"

"No," Zhang Jiuge replied.

"Do you have any skills?"

"I can only let others be happy."

Prince Yan burst out laughing, and gave him a gift of expensive wine.

Several years passed until Zhang Jiuge came to the residence of Prince Yan again. He announced that he was about to depart on a long journey, whereupon Prince Yan prepared a farewell banquet for him.

During the banquet, Zhang Jiuge said to Prince Yan: "May I amuse Your Highness with some of my trifling skills?"

He asked for a bolt of brocade and a pair of scissors. He then cut the brocade into shapes of bees and butterflies. No sooner had he finished cutting out one than it began to fly. Soon swarms of bees and butterflies were flying all round the hall. Some stuck to Prince Yan's robe, some perched on the hairpins of serving maids, and others flew freely in the air. Prince Yan was delighted with this entertainment.

Not long afterwards, Zhang Jiuge said, "Let me take them back; otherwise Prince Yan's brocade will be lost."

Then he gathered all the bees and butterflies up with his hand and turned them back into a roll of brocade. However, one end of the brocade in the shape of a butterfly was missing.

Prince Yan asked, "When will this butterfly come back?"

"This butterfly has been caught by someone in your residence, so it will not come back. Even if it does come back, it will leave a mark on the brocade."

Realizing that Zhang Jiuge had magic powers, Prince Yan asked him how long he would live. The other replied that the prince would live as long as the Buddhist shrine at the Kaibao Temple survived. After the two had drunk to their hearts' content, Zhang Jiuge stood up and took his leave.

Many years later, the Buddhist shrine in the Kaibao Temple callapsed. On that very day Prince Yan died, although he had not been ill in any way.

Abandoning an Official
Career for the Tao

Liu Xuanying, styled Zongcheng, was a native of Yanshan (Wanping, to the southwest of Beijing) in the Five Dynasties (907-960). In his youth he studied the classics and knew history well. Later he was a successful candidate in the highest imperial examination, and served as prime minister under Liu Shouguang, king of the State of Yan.

One day a Taoist came to his residence. Liu Xuanying entertained him with all courtesy, but when he asked him his name, the visitor refused to answer.

Then the Taoist asked Liu to have 10 eggs and 10 gold coins brought. He made a miniature pagoda with the eggs and coins.

Liu understood immediately that the Taoist wanted to inform him of some impending disaster.

The Taoist then said, "A high-ranking official with his feet on dangerous ground is in great danger." So saying, the Taoist broke the eggs one after another and left.

Liu Xuanying suddenly saw the light. On that

very day he packed up, abandoned all his money, handed in his seal and resigned his post. He left his residence early the following day.

After his resignation, Liu Xuanying visited Mount Taishan, Mount Huashan and Mount Nanshan to cultivate himself. Legend has it that he took Lü Dongbin as his teacher, and got to know some eminent Taoists, such as Zhang Wumeng, Zhong Fang and Chen Tuan. Later he lived in seclusion on Phoenix Peak in Daizhou Prefecture.

During the Tiansheng reign period (1023-1032) of Emperor Renzong of the Song Dynasty, he paid a visit to the Shouning Taoist Temple, where he wrote a poem. It reads:

If you don't read Taoist books,
How can you make pills of immortality?
Residing in the bustling city by myself,
I decline all invitations.
Growing crops and brewing wine
Are the only things immortals do.
I lie under the pine tree,
And live in leisure on White Cloud Ridge.

The poem is simple, unsophisticated and elegant. Still today, Liu Xuanying's calligraphy reading Shou Shan Fu Hai (Longevity Hill and Fortune Sea) can still be seen in the Qingyang Palace in Chengdu.

Liu Xuanying was one of the five founding fathers of Taoism in North China. Legend has it that he later became an immortal.

Portrait of a Taoist

Qutu Wuwei, also known as Shenhezi, lived in the Five Dynasties period. He was renowned for making pills of immortality.

An official named Zhang Zhongding once made a tour of the Eastern Capital (Luoyang) together with Shenhezi in his youth. Zhang did not know what Shenhezi was, but Shenhezi admired Zhang Zhongding's personality. During the tour the two went to restaurants every day to drink wine and discuss philosophy. Finally the day came when the two friends had to say good-bye to each other. Zhang Zhongding said to Shenhezi:

"Though this is the first time we have met, we are now intimate friends. But I still don't know your name. We might not meet again after we bid farewell to each other today." It seemed that Zhang Zhongding could not bear to part with Shenhezi.

Shenhezi told him his name. He also said that they would meet in Chengdu in the future. The two then parted from each other.

During the Zhenghe reign period (1111-1118) of Emperor Huizong of the Song Dynasty, Zhang

Zhongding was appointed governor of Chengdu. He was immediately reminded of Shenhezi's words that they would meet again in Chengdu. Zhang Zhongding wondered how Shenhezi could know about such a meeting beforehand. So he sent his men to look for Shenhezi everywhere, but they failed to find him.

While waiting for his friend, Zheng Zhongding had the Tianqing Taoist Temple and the Looking-for-the-Immortal Pavilion built. In his spare time, he often went there to wait for Shenhezi, and sometimes he would spend whole days there.

As Zhang Zhongding's term of office was about to come to an end, there was still no sight of Shenhezi. Zhang decided to go to the Looking-for-the-Immortal Pavilion every day to wait before leaving his post. He thought if Shenhezi did not show up, it meant that he had forgotten him.

At a loss what to do, Zhang Zhongding walked out of the pavilion to a corridor in the east, finding that the corridor was connected with a small Taoist temple. Zhang Zhongding walked toward the temple. It was empty, except for some dust-covered portraits of ancient people. Zhang Zhongding swept away the dust, and saw that one of these long-dead Taoists was the exact likeness of his friend. The inscription on the portrait read, "Shenhezi." All of a sudden, Zhang Zhongding was overtaken by an eerie feeling.

Falling Down from a Donkey

Chen Tuan (?-989) was a Taoist who lived in the period which saw the later Five Dynasties (907-960) give way to the Northern Song Dynasty (960-1127). One day, while riding a donkey along a street in Chang'an (present-day Xi'an), he encountered two persons, at the sight of whom he was so overjoyed that he fell off his donkey.

He cried out, "There is an emperor after all!"

These two persons were none other than Zhao Kuangyin, who later became Emperor Taizu of the Song Dynasty and ruled the country from 960 to 976, and his prime minister Zhao Pu (922-992).

Chen Tuan invited the pair to dine with him in a nearby wineshop. There he seated Zhao Kuangyin in the seat of honor.

Some time later, Chen Tuan learned that Zhao Kuangyin had indeed become emperor. He thereupon announced, "From now on the country will be peaceful and stable." He then wrote a poem, which reads: Having slept for forty years/I find the sun has risen in the east.

Soon afterwards, he went to Mount Huashan

and lived in seclusion. He declined time and again when Emperor Taizu tried to appoint him an official.

From *Records of Mr. Xiyi
on Mount Huashan*

Five Dragons Listen to
The Book of Changes

In his childhood, Chen Tuan once drank the milk of an old lady in a green gown.

"I shall make you a sage without material desires," the old lady said to him.

After Chen Tuan grew up, he began to study the classics and poetry, preparing for the imperial examination. During the Changxing reign period (930-933) of the Tang Dynasty, he took part in the highest imperial examination, but failed. Then he withdrew from society and lived in solitude in the Wudang Mountains, where he practiced Taoism for more than 20 years.

In the still of the night, Chen Tuan often burned incense and read *The Book of Changes* in the moonlight. One night he found five white-haired men with weird facial features sitting around him and listening to him read the book.

When he inquired as to who they were, one of them answered, "We are the dragons who live in the Sun and Moon Pool in the mountains. It is where the immortals of North China often gather. The ideal place for you to live in seclusion is Mount Huashan." No sooner had the old man finished saying this than the visitors disappeared.

A few days later, when Chen Tuan was sitting still to cultivate his physical and mental capabilities according to Taoist rules, the five old men appeared again.

"Close your eyes," they ordered him.

Chen Tuan closed his eyes obediently. All of a sudden, he rose high into the sky, and flew with the wind. Soon he arrived at Mount Huashan, in Shaanxi Province. When Chen Tuan opened his eyes, he found himself sitting on a rock, with no sign of the five old men.

Dragons are good at sleeping. Legend has it that Chen Tuan learnt sleeping skills from the five dragons.

On Mount Huashan Chen Tuan often shut himself up and sat cross-legged to meditate. He was able to sit for over 100 days at a time without moving. Upon learning of this, Emperor Shizong (reigned 954-959) of the Later Zhou Dynasty summoned Chen Tuan to the palace, and shut him up in a room to see if what he had heard was true. One month later, when the door was opened, Chen Tuan was still sleeping. Then he asked Chen Tuan to make pills of immortality for him.

"Your Majesty is the ruler of the country. You should always keep the people in your heart, rather than pills of immortality," was Chen Tuan's response.

Emperor Shizong was very unhappy at this, but

117

could not help it; he had to let Chen Tuan go back to Mount Huashan. Before Chen Tuan left, the emperor bestowed on him the name Mr. White Cloud, and ordered local officials to pay homage to him at a certain season every year.

From *On the Gardens* and *Records of Mr. Xiyi on Mount Huashan*

Preferring Sleep to Beauties

For the first few years after he was born, Chen Tuan was not able to speak. At the age of five, one day he met an old lady in a green garment by a river. The old lady pulled him closer and gave him her breast. After that, Chen Tuan began to open his mouth to speak and became very intelligent. By the time he was 15, he had read *The Book of Songs*, *The Book of Historical Documents*, *The Book of Changes*, *The Book of Rites* and many medical books. After his parents died, Chen Tuan, who was not satisfied with what he had learnt, was determined to take a trip throughout the empire to confer with Taoist immortals under the pine tree at the top of Mount Taishan and make pills of immortality. So he gave away all his property and left home with only a stone jar.

Scholars and officials of the Later Tang Dynasty (923-936), who had admired Chen Tuan for a long time because he was aloof from politics and material pursuits, were eager to meet him. But Chen Tuan was not interested in knowing them. Every day he led a carefree life. In ordinary dress, he roamed about the streets and drank in wineshops during the daytime, and stayed at small inns at night.

Emperor Mingzong (reigned 926-933) of the Later Tang Dynasty, who had long known about Chen Tuan, summoned him to the palace one day. The emperor bestowed on him the name "Recluse Qingxu," and presented him with two palace maidens as gifts. Then Chen Tuan wrote a petition to the emperor, saying, "These girls are from good families. Once they enter the palace, they should enjoy glory, splendor, wealth and a good life. Now Your Majesty wishes them to serve me, as if they had fallen from Heaven to Earth. Your humble subject does not dare to accept. I am like a deer preferring a wandering life. I hope Your Majesty will let me return to my humble abode." He also attached a poem to his petition. It read:

> They have snow-white skin and jade-like cheeks.
> I am grateful to Your Majesty for presenting
>   them to me.
> I, a hermit scholar, do not even dream of
>   material things,
> So I am afraid that they will be useless to me.

He handed the petition in, and left. Later he lived at Jiushiyan in the Wudang Mountains to cultivate himself for more than 20 years.

Later, he went to Mount Huashan. In the dead of night, a golden man holding a sword appeared in his courtyard and said to him:

"You have finished your cultivation. You should have a home to return to."

"All things on earth will disappear in autumn. At that time I will settle down," Chen Tuan replied.

Later Chen Tuan moved to the Cloud and Terrace Taoist Temple on Mount Huashan.

There he had a friend, Cui Gu. One day a man called Jin Li came to pay a visit to Cui Gu. Jin Li admired Chen Tuan very much and hoped Cui Gu would introduce him to Chen Tuan.

Cui Gu replied, "Mr. Chen Tuan has just fallen asleep. You may meet him after he wakes up."

"How long he will sleep?" Jin Li asked.

"Maybe half a year, or three or four months — more than a month at least. If you have something to do, you'd better do it first; then you can come back to see him."

Over a year later, Jin Li came to Mount Huashan again. It happened that Chen Tuan had just come home from a trip. Seeing Chen Tuan, Jin Li fell to his knees, and said:

"I came to Mount Huashan to see you last year, but you were sleeping soundly. Could you please tell me if you practice Taoism while asleep?" Jin Li asked.

Chen Tuan burst out laughing, and then sat down cross-legged: "If you don't have common knowledge about daily life and sleep, it will be very difficult for you to avoid death. As for sleep, there is a song about it:

For ordinary people,
Nothing is more important than sleep.
Immortals do not sleep,
In dreams they travel on clouds and with the
mist.
There are always pills of immortality on the
stove;
And there is another world in the wine pot.
If you want to know about my dream,
I would say it's the most wonderful thing on
earth."

He then said, "I want to sleep now. Please come back in a few days, when you will see what real sleep is."

A few days later, Jin Li came back again. He found Chen Tuan lying on his back without breathing. The hermit had rosy cheeks, and his body was surrounded by a brilliant luster. Jin Li simply bowed to him and left.

One fine spring day Chen Tuan took a tour of Mount Huashan with his good friends Hu Gong, Chi Songzi and Lü Dongbin. When they sat down to take a rest, the local god of the land came and presented them with wine and fresh fruit. The four immortals began to compose poems while drinking wine. Hu Gong was the first to recite, as follows:

In my wine pot there are towers and terraces
Surrounded by beautiful flowers all the year
round.
I drink wine whenever I have time,

And lie on a moss-covered stone, inebriated.
I am leisurely and carefree
And don't seek fame and gain.
I don't discuss current affairs with anyone I
    meet,
I only smile and point at the floating clouds.

Chi Songzi's poem went as follows:

I have just left my bamboo hut in the mountain,
And passed by the old Yintian Terrace.
Wine has just been warmed in the cave,
And the wayside flowers are in full bloom.
I am not an ordinary person,
But a man of moral integrity and an immortal.
I don't discuss current affairs with anyone I
    meet,
I only smile and point at the floating clouds.

Lü Dongbin then chimed in with:

Out of luck, I came here,
Since then a few years have elapsed.
I buy wine whenever I'm unhappy,
And drink to my heart's content.
I have roamed for 81 days,
And once went to Lord Mao's terrace drunk.
I don't discuss current affairs with anyone I
    meet,
I only smile and point at the floating clouds.

Chen Tuan was very proud of his ability to sleep. He sang:

123

In the warm spring flowers are in full bloom,
As I roam among rocky mountains.
I once admired jade inscriptions and golden
   gates,
While setting foot on sand and green moss,
I slept several years in a cave,
And drank a thousand cups of wine.
I don't discuss current affairs with anyone I
   meet,
I only smile and point at the floating clouds.

The Magic Flutes

In the Kaiyuan reign period (713-741) of the Tang Dynasty, Lü Xiangyun, a merchant, lived by Lake Dongting. Every year he took goods to sell in Jiangxi Province, and brought back goods from Jiangxi to sell in Hunan Province. He only put aside one tenth of his profits for his own use, distributing the rest among his poor relatives and poverty-stricken neighbors.

Lü Xiangyun was an expert flute player. On business trips, whenever he came across beautiful scenery he would stop his boat, take out his flute and play a few tunes. One spring, on his way to Jiangxi, Lü Xiangyun anchored his boat at the foot of Mount Junshan at the mouth of Lake Dongting at dusk. He asked the boatman to prepare some wine for him. Sitting on the deck, he enjoyed himself, drinking wine and playing his flute. After a while, he saw a fishing boat approaching. In it there was an old man with snow-white brows and beard. Xiangyun hastily put down his flute and stood up to welcome him. The old man then boarded Xiangyun's boat.

"I heard the beautiful sound of your flute from

far away, so I followed the sound here," the old man said.

After an exchange of conventional greetings, Xiangyun invited the old man to drink wine with him.

After a while, the stranger told Xiangyun that he himself was a flute player, and produced three flutes from his sleeve. One was an ordinary flute, another was a long double flute, and the third was short and thin, about the size of a writing brush. When Xiangyun asked him to play the flutes, the old man explained, "The longest one can only be used in Heaven, to accompany other divine musical instruments," the old man replied. "If it were to be blown on earth, there would be landslides, the sun and moon would lose their light, the stars would be in great disorder, and mountains would collapse. The medium-sized flute is used to accompany immortal music in the place where immortals gather, such as Penglai Fairyland and Gushe Mountain. If it were to be blown on earth, sand and stones would fly, birds would fall to the ground, the brains of animals would split open, and human beings would die on hearing the sound. I only play this short flute to my friends on earth."

So saying, the old man began to blow the short flute. At only the third note, a strong wind blew, clouds scudded across the sky and terrifying waves arose. Fish and turtles were thrown heavenward. Xiangyun and his servants heard a deafening noise, which terrified them. As the old man continued to blow the flute, the birds and animals began chirping and howling. Then the moonlight became dim and the boat seemed to turn over. Xiangyun was so frightened that he did not know what to do. The old man drank several cups of wine, and then said to Xiangyun: "I shall meet you at the temple fair next spring."

With this, he went back to his fishing boat, and disappeared in the mist.

Xiangyun failed to keep the appointment the next spring. He did not go back to Mount Junshan until the autumn. He lingered there for 10 days, but failed to meet the old man.

From *Records of Strange Things*

Li Jing Produces Rain

At the end of the Sui Dynasty (581-618), Li
Jing, who later became a famous general and made
great contributions to the founding of the Tang
Dynasty, lived in a village near Mount Huoshan.
An old man living in the same village, who seemed
to have perceived something unusual in him, often
gave him financial help. The friendship between
them grew with each passing day. Li Jing was
particularly fond of hunting. One day, he spotted a
herd of deer, which he followed until he lost both
the herd and his way in the gathering dusk.
Dispirited, he wondered where he might spend the
night. Suddenly he spied a light in the distance. He
quickened his steps and came in sight of a grand
mansion enclosed by high walls and with a large
red gate. He knocked, but a long time passed before
a servant answered. Li Jing explained that he was
lost and asked for permission to stay the night. It
might be improper, the servant said, for his masters
were out and only Her Ladyship, the dowager, and
womenfolk were at home. Li begged him: "Could
you please convey my appeal to the dowager and
see what she says?"

Presently, the servant returned and said, "The dowager does not like to have strangers in the house, especially at night. But, considering your situation, she thinks it better to allow you to stay."

Li was shown into the reception hall. A maid came in to announce the dowager. The lady was in her fifties, and wore a cloud-white blouse over a sea-blue gown. She carried an air of nobility as if she were a lady of aristocratic birth. Li stepped forward and bowed.

The lady said, "You must understand, sir, that it is inadvisable to invite a man in while my sons are away. But as you've strayed to our place at this late hour, it is inappropriate to deny you shelter. I hope you won't mind the coarseness of our mountain life. If you do hear some commotion at night, don't be alarmed. That will be my sons coming home."

Dinner was then served. The food was excellent, with many fish courses. After dinner, Li Jing was led by a maid to a guest room. He was unable to sleep, thinking, who would make a fanfare returning home at night in this remote mountain village?

He sat awake in the room with his ears pricked up.

After midnight, an urgent knocking was heard at the gate, and someone responded. "Heavenly mandate!" Another voice blared. "Big son, immediately produce rain in the two hundred mile area around this mountain till five o'clock in the morning. No delay, and no deluge!"

A servant must have passed on the message, for the dowager said: "It couldn't have come at a worse moment. Neither son is home yet. Even if messengers were dispatched right away, they would not be able to return in time. Any negligence of duty or delay of action will be reprimanded, and it certainly is inappropriate to have a servant execute the heavenly mandate by proxy. What shall we do now?"

A quick-witted maid interjected: "The guest we entertained this evening seemed to have some extraordinary traits. Perhaps we can ask him to do it."

It seemed that the idea appealed to the dowager, for she came in person and tapped on Li Jing's door. "Are you awake, sir? Can I have a word with you?" she said.

Li Jing came out.

The dowager said, "You might have realized that ours is not a human abode. As a matter of fact, you are in a dragon palace. My elder son has gone to the East China Sea to attend a wedding ceremony, and my younger son is escorting his sister to her husband's. As both sons are thousands of miles away, it is impossible to call them back in time. What's more, I can't find a gentleman surrogate. I wonder if I can enlist your immediate assistance."

"I'm just an ordinary mortal," Li Jing said. "I can't ride the clouds. How can I produce rain? But,

131

if Your Ladyship can teach me how, I am at your service."

"I will tell you what to do. It is not as difficult as you think." She ordered the groom to saddle a piebald horse and fetch what she called the "rain-producer," which turned out to be a small bottle. Hanging the bottle on the pommel, she said, "Ride this horse. Just give it a free rein. When it paws and neighs, pour out a drop of liquid from the bottle onto its mane. Remember: One drop is enough."

He mounted, and the horse cantered off. Not realizing that he was already in the clouds, he wondered at the smoothness of the ride. High winds whistled past like arrows; thunderbolts flashed from beneath the horse's hooves. He poured out a drop of liquid from the bottle whenever the horse indicated. All of a sudden, the clouds split apart, and he saw right below him a village where he had once sojourned. For years, the villagers there had been very kind to him, and he had long been torn by the thought that he was not in a position to repay their hospitality. Now that he was in charge of rain, and their crops were scorched by a severe drought, why should he begrudge giving them a little extra? What is one tiny drop of water to such a thirst? So he sprinkled out 20 drops.

After a while his job was done, and he returned to the dragon palace. The dowager met him at the hall with tear-filled eyes.

"Why did you let me down? I told you that one drop would be enough. How could you act willfully and mete out 20!

One drop from this bottle means a foot of rain on the ground. You made a flood of 20 feet in the dead of night. Do you think anyone can survive that? I've already been punished. Look, 80 lashes across my back!" Blood was oozing through the back of her blouse. "My sons were punished, too. They were put into prison. What can we do now?"

Li Jing was too ashamed to even mumble an excuse. After a while, the dowager sighed and said, "You are only mortal and have no idea how divine things work. I don't blame you, but I'm afraid Master Dragon will try to punish you. You had better leave now. However, since I requested your service, I'm not going to send you away empty-handed. Though we don't have treasures hoarded in this mountain residence, I will offer you two slaves. You can take both, or pick one as you please."

At her call, two slaves emerged. One stepped forth from the east chamber, beaming amiably; the other stalked out from the west chamber, his face dark with anger. Li Jing thought to himself: I'm a hunter and take pride in physical strength. If I should choose the amiable one, people would laugh behind my back, ridiculing me as chicken-hearted. So he said, "Thank you, Madam. One will be enough. I'll take the angry fellow."

"He is yours," said the dowager with an elusive smile.

Li Jing bade her farewell and left with the slave. Several steps out of the gate, he glanced back. The mansion and walls were all gone. He whirled round to question the slave, but the slave had vanished too!

By dawn, he managed to get back to where the village had once stood. A vast expanse of water greeted his eyes, only the tops of a few big trees remaining above the surface. No one could have survived. Li Jing was very sad when he saw this.

Later Li Jing became a seasoned general and helped the new emperor quell many revolts and border incidents. His feats were unsurpassed, and yet, he never reached the position of prime minister. A popular saying has it that prime ministers are born in the more cultured east, while great generals arise in the rougher west.

From *Records of the Taiping Era*

A Goddess Gives Huang Di Tallies

Huang Di (the Yellow Emperor), whose surname was Gongsun, was the common ancestor of all the ethnic groups of the Chinese nation. He was the second son of Gongsun Shaodian, the king of the Bear Kingdom, and his mother was Xiqiao Fubiao. Four to five thousand years ago, Xiqiao Fubiao became pregnant when she dreamed of a large ring of light around the Big Dipper, illuminating the earth. After she had been pregnant for 24 months, she gave birth to a baby and named it Tianshu.

In his childhood, Tianshu was very intelligent. He could walk very quickly and was good at talking. He grew up as an honest, intelligent and handsome man with a high forehead, wide shoulders and white skin. At first, he lived by the Jishui River and took Da Xiang as his teacher. At the age of 15 he knew everything in the world, and was given the title Huang Di and hereditary territory. As he had engaged in manufacturing *xuanmian* (cart canopies), he styled himself Xuanyuan.

He married Xiling Leizu at Daliang. She gave birth to two sons—one was named Xuanxiao, and the other Changyi. Though Huang Di was supported and loved by the people of the whole country, he still kept the true qualities of the laboring people. Without being ordered to, people all over the country united around Huang Di. The emperor handled state affairs in a down-to-earth style. Under his rule, the country was peaceful and prosperous; the people respected and helped with each other; and nobody locked his door.

In the 22nd year after Huang Di came to power, Chiyou suddenly rose in revolt against him. Chiyou was the chief of the most powerful tribe in the land. He had 80 brothers, each of whom looked like an animal but could speak. With copper heads and iron cheeks, they did not eat grain like ordinary people, but swallowed sand and stones. They disobeyed Huang Di's decrees and set up a code of five cruel punishments. In addition, they dug gold mines on Mount Gelu, smelted ore and produced armor, swords, knives and halberds to threaten the people all over the country. Huang Di sent armed forces to suppress them. However after 15 years' efforts, Huang Di had still conquered Chiyou. One night he dreamed that a strong wind blew dust up from the ground, and a man was driving a herd of sheep holding a huge arrow in one hand. When he woke up, he had wise men interpret the dream. They said that two men would come to help him—one named Feng Hou (meaning after the wind), and the other Li Mu (meaning a herdsman with great power). Eventually, Feng Hou was found at the end of the sea and Li Mu in a big lake. The emperor appointed Feng Hou as his minister of civil affairs, and later promoted him to prime minister. Li Mu he made command-in-chief. In cooperation with Yugang, an eighth-generation descendent of Shennong (the Divine Farmer), Huang Di mounted another campaign against Chiyou. The war was fought for quite a long time, but Huang Di still could not defeat Chiyou. Disappointed and unhappy, Huang Di had to return to the foot of Mount Taishan. One day, the emperor dreamed that a person in a fox-fur coat, an envoy from the Queen Mother of the West, presented a tally to him, saying "He who has this tally will be invincible." As soon as the emperor woke up, he had an altar set up. He knelt before it holding a tally and a green piece of cloth three inches wide and one foot long with characters written on it in blood, and prayed to Heaven for victory over Chiyou. His sincerity moved Heaven. After three days and nights of heavy fog, a goddess with the body of a bird came down from Heaven. The Yellow Emperor stepped forward and bowed. "I am Xuannü," the girl said, and gave him 300 scriptures. "March once more against Chiyou after having read these scriptures for a hundred days. Now I give you two tallies. Wear them, and you will defeat Chiyou." Huang Di then ordered Feng Hou to drill the army and also tried to use music for martial ends. When everything was ready, Huang Di led his army against Chiyou. Chiyou was defeated and killed at Banquan (near present-day Zhulu in Hebei Province). The emperor had his head buried at Shouzhang, his arms and shoulders at Shanyang, and his legs at Julu.

Later, Yugang challenged Huang Di for the throne. After 52 battles Huang Di emerged victorious.

After the unification of the country, the emperor devoted himself to construction. He was busy cutting into mountains and building roads day and night. He ordered Feng Hou to carry a sword and make investigations of the geographical conditions and people's lives of the whole empire. Feng Hou set out early every morning and came back late every night, walking 10,000 *li* (1 *li* = 1/2 km) a day. The Yellow Emperor, who also tried to learn from the immortals, kowtowed to them and said, "Feng Hou is eager to know about the rivers." One god replied, "There are five rivers in China. They all originate in the Kunlun Mountains. One of them is the Yellow River, which originates at the southeastern foot of the Kunlun Mountains." The Yellow Emperor dispatched Shu Hai to measure the territory by paces. From the east to the west totaled 500,019,800 steps; and from the south to the north, 200,031,300 steps. Shu Hai also tried to measure the territory to the north of Mount Qingqiu, from Mount Taishan in the east to the neighboring countries in the west. The measurement showed that from the east to the west was 28,000 *li*, and from the south to the north,

26,000 *li*. When this work was completed, the Yellow Emperor began to set up prefectures and counties.

Some magic grass grew in the imperial palace, which would indicate whenever a crafty and evil person entered. A foreign country sent an animal as tribute to the Yellow Emperor. The animal looked like a deer, but it only had one horn. At the sight of a treacherous court official, the animal would run at him. Thus, no evil persons dared to approach the emperor. Rongchengzi, a descendant of Nüwa (a goddess who once patched up the sky), knew Taoist doctrines and music well. He was appointed Master Musician, and devoted himself to composing music. Later, he held a large concert in the open area by Dongting Lake. The Yellow Emperor himself was an accomplished musician. He often played in a heavenly orchestra, when 16 pairs of cranes danced around him. Beimencheng said, "The music played by the Yellow Emperor can mediate *yin* and *yang*; make the sun and moon shine; and harmonize local customs."

The Queen Mother of the West, the daughter of the Heavenly Emperor, had a human body, a tiger's head, a leopard's tail and white hair. She often howled. She lived in the Golden Terrace in Stone City, and often sat on Shaoguang Mountain, with three green birds fetching food for her. The Queen Mother of the West, who admired the Yellow Emperor, went to see him, riding a white deer, and presented him with a white jade ring. Another god rode a white deer from the south to offer the Yellow Emperor a magic beast called Chang, because he believed the emperor was the embodiment of justice and virtue. He once ate a red fruit in the shape of the Chinese flowering crabapple, and tasting like a plum. Legend has it that one who tasted this fruit would never drown. The Yellow Emperor built a terrace on the mountain where the Queen Mother of the West lived in Woren Kingdom, and named it Xuanyuan Terrace, where he could take a rest. Later he paid a visit to the Huaxu Kingdom of the immortals, and then settled down in the Tiandu Kingdom, which was also known as the Xuanyuan Kingdom. The Yellow Emperor continued his journey to the Qiongshan Kingdom of Women in the west, to the Kunlun Palace in the north, and to the sea and Mount Huanshan in the east. By the sea he met a magic beast, which knew everything on earth. The emperor asked it to write a book about the devils and gods it knew to warn all the people in the country. The Yellow Emperor himself wrote a passage cursing evil. During his travels around the country, his wife died. The Yellow Emperor then made her an ancestral goddess. As the country was peaceful and prosperous, he went to Mount Taishan to offer sacrifices for its meritorious service, held a memorial ceremony for Yan Di, studied astronomy and geography, put palace affairs under control, had clothes made, discovered the law of the changes in meteorological phenomena, and went in for large-scale construction. Thanks to his great contributions, the Heavenly Emperor granted him clothes, weapons, a sedan chair and an immortal's hillock.

From *Accounts of the Saints*

Peng Zu Explains the Way
to Keep in Good Health

At the end of the Shang Dynasty (c. 16th-11th centuries B.C.), there was a palace maiden who knew the secret of preserving her health. Though she was more than 270 years old, she still looked like a young girl. The ruler took her as his teacher and built a special mansion decorated with gold and jade for her.

In addition, he sent her to ask Peng Zu about the way to live forever, riding in a carriage with a heavy curtain specially used by noblewomen. Legend has it that Peng Zu was an immortal. He told her: "If one wants to go to Heaven to be a celestial, one should take the golden pills of immortality. The pills are prepared for the immortals living in the Yuqing Fairyland. One who takes such pills will go to Heaven in the daytime. The king cannot compared with the immortals, who are imbued with Taoist doctrines. He should cultivate his spirit and eat cakes made with medicines that prolong life. In this way he could live longer but could not send a ghost or a god on an errand nor travel on the wind."

Peng Zu continued: "Taking medicine will not be helpful to those who do not know about sexual intercourse between men and women. Everyone can know about the relations between *yin* and *yang* by inference. I was a posthumous child. At the age of three, my mother died. During the war in the west, I became destitute and homeless, and came to the Western Regions. Since then more than a hundred years have passed. I have so far lost 49 wives and 54 children. A multitude of worries and sufferings have injured my internal *qi* and made my skin dry up. I wonder if I can live much longer. In addition, I have very meager knowledge. So I am not able to teach others how to prolong their lives. On Mount Dawan here in the Western Regions there lives Mr. Qing Jing. It is said that he is 1,000 years old now, but he looks like a lad, and can walk 300 *li* a day. He can go for a year without eating anything, and can also eat nine meals a day. Why don't you go to ask him about the way to live long?"

Upon hearing this, the palace maiden asked, "Could you please tell me what kind of celestial that worthy is?"

"Mr. Qing Jing is not a celestial," Peng Zu replied. "He is only a Taoist. A so-called celestial is one who can fly in the sky without wings; or float up to Heaven riding a magic dragon; or turn into a bird or a beast to travel in the clouds, swim in the river or the sea, or circle in the mountains; or absorb primordial *qi* and eat glossy ganoderma and other herbs; or live unnoticed among ordinary people and; or withdraw from society and live in solitude. The so-called celestial has a face and bones different from those of ordinary people, their fine hair being different from the others'. They love to stay in quiet and remote places, shunning ordinary people. However, though celestials enjoy long lives, they have no human feelings, and are strangers to honor and shame. It is just as if a sparrow turned into a toad. It would change all its original features, and all its internal organs. That is not what I am longing for right now."

Peng Zu continued: "After one has accepted primordial *qi*, one can live 120 years without knowing Taoist magic. If one cannot live such a long life, it means one's primordial *qi* is injured. One who knows Taoist magic will enjoy a life of 240 years, or even 480 years. One who knows Taoist magic perfectly will live forever, but will not become an immortal. The way to keep in good health is to avoid injuring primordial *qi*. Keeping warm in winter and cool in summer benefits the health. One who wants to keep his primordial *qi* must not be addicted to beautiful girls or to comfort, and must avoid ostentation and extravagance, which indicates one's status. One should be content with one's lot with concentrated attention. Musical instruments made of gold, stone, silk, bamboo, earth, leather and wood, and the various colors— green, red, yellow, white and black—can please people's visual and aural senses and are helpful for prolonging people's life. All material enjoyment will do harm to those who do not adopt the above-mentioned methods and have no sense of propriety. Those who know how to control themselves and discharge wastes will keep fit and prolong their lives. For instance water and fire are indispensable to people's life. However too much water and fire is harmful. One falls sick if one's main and collateral channels are injured, the vital energy and blood are insufficient, the internal organs do not work well and the marrow and cerebrospinal fluid are insufficient. Thinking and memorizing too much will do harm to people's health; excessive worrying and sadness will injure the spirit; excessive joy and delight, and anger and sorrow will be harmful to the health; too eager desire, and lack of care about changes of temperature and irregular interchanges between *yin* and *yang* will also harm the health. Regarding sexual intercourse between a married couple as causing serious harm is erroneous. Sexual intercourse between a couple is as natural as Heaven and Earth. As Heaven and Earth follow the law of combination, Earth can move forever. If human beings do not have a good command of the law of connection, people will fall sick, get injured and die. If people can avoid all things that are harmful to the health, and have a good command of the combinations between *yin* and *yang*, immortality is possible. There are 365 days and 365 nights in a year, during which there are four times for the intercourse of Heaven and Earth. Hence all things on the earth can live on the earth forever. If mankind can take the intercourse between Heaven and Earth as the norm, human beings can live forever.

"In addition, people have to deal with lots of affairs. Only a few can afford to be disillusioned with the mortal world and retire to the mountains. If they are taught with Taoist magic, they will not master it. This is not the real intention of people with lofty ideals. Therefore, understanding sexual intercourse between men and women, mastering the way to cultivate themselves, reducing worries and thinking, and controlling the intake of food and drink are the ways to keep in good health."

Upon returning to the palace, the palace maiden conveyed Peng Zu's teachings to the Shang ruler. After following Peng Zu's instructions for a period of time, his health was greatly improved. Overjoyed, the king decided to keep Peng Zu's teachings to himself alone. He ordered that all those who knew Peng Zu's formula for healthy living be killed. He even tried to kill Peng Zu, but Peng Zu escaped.

From *Accounts of the Saints* • *Peng Zu*

Lady Gouyi

Lady Gouyi was a concubine of Emperor Wudi and mother of Emperor Zhaodi of the Han Dynasty (206 B.C.-A.D. 25). She was born in the State of Qi and lived in Hejian (in the southeast of present-day Xianxian County, Hebei Province). In her childhood, she was bed-ridden for six years. She ate little, and her fists were always clenched.

One day Emperor Wudi (reigned 140-87 B.C.) went hunting. As he passed Hejian, a necromancer, who was good at recognizing omens by observing the air above a place, said to the emperor: "According to the air in the northeast, there must be a noble girl there." Emperor Wudi sent envoys to look for the girl, and finally beautiful Gouyi was found. She was escorted to the capital, Chang'an. At the sight of such a beautiful girl, Emperor Wudi was overjoyed and went over to hold her by the hand. To his surprise, he found that it was like grasping a pair of jade hooks. Then, for the first time in her life, Gouyi's hands slowly uncurled. The emperor, who was very fond of this beautiful girl, named her "Lady Fist," and promoted her to be a high-ranking imperial concubine. Soon afterwards "Lady Fist" gave birth to a son, Liu Fuling, who later succeeded to the throne and became Emperor Zhaodi.

Some time later, "Lady Fist" lived in the Sweet Spring Palace together with Emperor Wudi. To prevent her from holding court from behind a screen like Queen Lü of Emperor Gaozu, who threw the country into confusion, the emperor severely punished her on the excuse of a tiny error, and finally let her take her own life. During the month when the corpse was lying in state in the palace, it remained soft and emitted a sweet odor.

After Emperor Zhaodi came to the throne, he conferred upon his mother the title of Empress Dowager. He dispatched 20,000 laborers to build a tomb for her and picked an auspicious day to have his mother buried. However when Lady Gouyi was reburied, only a pair of silk shoes were found in the coffin. The palace building where she had once lived was renamed the Gouyi Palace, and later renamed Gouyi Temple. A shrine to her was built in the palace.

From *Accounts of the Saints* • *Lady Gouyi*

Mr. Fuju

There was a mirror-polisher named Mr. Fuju who often appeared at fairs in Wudi (present-day Suzhou). No one knew where he came from, but by his accent he originated in Hebei or Liaoning province.

When polishing mirrors for customers, Mr. Fuju always asked them if they had sick people at home. If he learnt that someone was sick, he would treat him or her with purple pills free of charge. All patients would soon recover after taking his medicine. One year, a pestilence prevailed in Wudi. Patients came to see Mr. Fuju in an endless stream. About 10,000 people were saved by him, but he never charged anyone a penny. Then the people of Wudi realized that Mr. Fuju was a Taoist immortal.

Later, Mr. Fuju went to live at the top of Mount Wushan. Whenever a patient came to see him, Mr. Fuju would hand down his pills from the mountaintop. Before Mr. Fuju left for Heaven, he said to his servant: "I am returning to the Penglai Fairyland. I shall provide you with some magic water later. "

Soon after Mr. Fuju passed away, water oozed

out from rocks nearby. Sick people in the locality found that they were soon cured after drinking some of this water. To commemorate Mr. Fuju's great deeds, local people vied with each to build shrines to him. Finally, more than 10 shrines to Mr. Fuju were set up.

From *Accounts of the Saints* • *Mr. Fuju*

Turning a Stone into Sheep

Huang Chuping was a native of Danxi. At the age of 15 he was sent to graze sheep. A certain Taoist who found him kind and prudent took him to a cave on Mount Jinhua where he lived for more than 40 years, completely forgetting his home. Huang Chuqi, his elder brother, looked for Chuping everywhere, but to no avail. Many years passed, then one day he met a fortune teller on the street, and asked him to use his supernatural powers to help him find Chuping.

The fortune teller said, "I once met a person called Huang Chuping on Mount Jinhua. Maybe he is your brother."

Huang Chuqi was very surprised to hear this. He lost no time sending people to Mount Jinhua to look for his brother. Chuping was found. When the two brothers met, Chuqi asked Chuping where his sheep were. Chuping said they were all on the east side of the mountain. Chuqi looked eastward, but saw only a vast expanse of white stones. He said to Chuping: "There are no sheep in the east."

"My sheep are all there, but you cannot see them," Chuping answered. He then murmured an incantation, and all the white stones turned into sheep.

Chuqi asked his brother to teach him the secrets of Taoism, to which request Chuping readily asserted.

Chuqi then abandoned his wife and children, and went to live on the mountain with Chuping. They ate pine and cypress leaves.

After 10,000 days, Chuqi reached the pinnacle of self-cultivation. He knew how to become invisible in broad daylight. Moreover, he always had a youthful appearance. Later, the two brothers paid a visit to their home, where they found almost all their relatives dead.

Before leaving for the mountain once more, they passed on the technique of making pills of immortality to Nan Bofeng, who was later renamed Chi Songzi. Later Chuqi was renamed Lu Ban, and Chuping, Song Zi.

From *Records of Immortals* • *Huang Chuping*

Boyang Makes Pills of Immortality

Wei Boyang was a native of Shangyu (in present-day Zhejiang Province). Though born into a noble family, he had no interest in wordly matters, devoting himself instead to the study of Taoism and self-cultivation.

One day, he took three disciples to the mountains to make pills of immortality. After pills of elixir were made, Wei Boyang said to them: "Now the pills of immortality have been made. Let's give some to a dog. If the dog goes up to heaven after having taken the pills, we may take them too. If it dies, we should not take them."

It turned out that there was a kind of special pill, "poisonous pills," made by Taoists. One who took the "poisonous pills" would play dead temporarily. Wei Boyang wanted to give his disciples a test. So when coming to the mountain, he brought some "poisonous pills" and a white dog with him. So saying Boyang fed the white dog a few "poisonous pills," and the white dog fell to the ground and "died" right away. Boyang said to his disciples: "We have made great efforts to make the pills of immortality. However the dog died after having

154

taken them. I am afraid we did not follow the god's instructions properly. What can we do if we die like the dog?"

"Teacher," the three disciples asked him, "will you take the pills of elixir?"

Boyang replied, "I have left home to make pills of immortality in the mountain. It runs counter to the common practice of the society. Since I can neither become an immortal nor go back home, life and death are same to me. I should take the pills." Then Wei Boyang took some pills of immortality. He fell to the ground and pretended to be dead.

Seeing it, the three disciples looked at each other in blank dismay. One said: "We came to the mountain to make the pills of immortality so as to live forever. Now we shall die immediately if we take the pills of elixir. What shall we do then?"

Another disciple responded: "Our master is not an ordinary person. Maybe he played dead purposely." After saying this, he took some "poisonous pills" too, fell to the ground and "died." The other two disciples discussed: "We hope to live a long life when we made the pills of immortality. Now they two lost their lives after having taken them. What's the use of these pills of immortality? We may continue to live several dozen of years without taking the pills." Both of them decided not to take the pills of elixir. Then they walked out of the mountain to buy coffins to bury the dead ones.

No sooner had the two disciples left, Wei

Boyang got up and put some pills of immortality into the mouths of his disciple and dog. Soon his disciple and dog came back to life, and became immortals with their master.

Later a person went deep into the mountain to cut some firewood, where he met Wei Boyang. Wei Boyang asked the woodcutter to deliver a letter to his two disciples to express his gratitude. Seeing his letter, the two disciples were felt remorse.

From *Records of Immortals* • *Wei Boyang*

Recovering Youthful Vigor

Bo Shanpu was a native of Yongzhou (in present-day Shaanxi Province). He practiced Taoism on Mount Huashan. Every day he concentrated himself on self-cultivation, eating only wild plants. He often went back to his hometown to see his relatives. Though he was over 200 years old, he looked young and vigorous.

As soon as Bo Shanpu entered a house, he could immediately identify the merits and errors of the family's ancestors, as if he had seen them with his own eyes. He could also foresee whether it would have good or bad luck. What he predicted always came true. Once, when staying at home, he found his niece old and feeble, so he offered her some special pills. Soon after she took them, his niece, who was over 70 years old, gradually became younger and younger in appearance. Finally she looked like a charming girl.

Later an envoy of the Han Dynasty (206 B.C.-A.D. 220) was traveling by the West River to the east of Yongzhou. There he saw a girl beating an old man with a whip. Shocked, the envoy demanded to know the reason for this outrageous behavior. The girl said: "He is my son. My uncle Bo Shanpu gave me some magic medicine which restored my youth and vigor. I want my son to take this magic medicine, but he refuses. He is old and weak, looking much older than I."

The envoy asked how old the woman and her son were. The woman replied, "I am 230 years old, and my son is only 70." Later Bo Shanpu's niece also went to Mount Huashan.

From *Records of Immortals* • *Bo Shanpu*

Yuzi Spurns the King's Offer

Yuzi, a native of Nanjun (in present-day Hubei Province), was fond of esoteric studies from childhood. King You (reigned 781-771 B.C.) of the Zhou Dynasty offered him an official post. But Yuzi turned it down. He said, "Every day we get closer and closer to death. If a person only seeks position and wealth, and does not know how to cultivate himself, he will be no better than ashes at the end of his life. What is the use of high rank or piles of gold and jade? To become an immortal means being able to enjoy eternal life."

Yuzi, who was determined to become an immortal, took Chang Sangzi as his teacher, and learned many Taoist magic arts from him. Yuzi himself also created a way to cultivate himself. He made use of the mutual-support and mutual-resistance properties of the five elements (metal, wood, water, fire and earth) to cultivate his moral character, cure diseases and avoid disasters. He could summon clouds and rain, start thunder and make fog gather. Whenever he went on journey with his disciples, he would make horses out of clay, give one to each, and tell them to close their eyes. The clay horses would instantly become real horses, which could travel 1,000 *li* a day. Legend has it that later Yuzi went to Mount Kongtong to make pills of immortality, and thus became an immortal.

From *Records of Immortals* • *Yuzi*

Looking for a Teacher

Taiyinnü, whose original name was Lu Quan, was a bright girl, understanding and considerate. She learned some of Yuzi's magic arts. In a search for a new teacher, she set up a stall by the roadside, selling wine to passers-by and hoping to find a person of talent to be her teacher. Many years passed, but she did not find one who was better than she at Taoist magic arts.

One day a learned Taoist called Taiyangzi passed her wine stall. He found Taiyinnü to be very polite and well spoken. Taiyangzi sighed, "She takes the White Tiger and Flying Snake Steps, while I adopt the Green Dragon and Tortoise Steps. The world is so large; who can really know its profound mysteries?"

Taiyinnü was very glad to hear this. She got her younger sister to ask Taiyangzi what was the number of "earth" in the five elements. Taiyangzi replied, "I don't know what its number is; I only know that 'earth' is one of the three elements in the south, of the five elements in the north, of the seven in the east and of the nine in the west."

Her younger sister conveyed Taiyangzi's words

to Taiyinnü, who asserted, "That customer must be a great person of virtue, and a highly skilled Taoist. You only asked him one element, but he knows all five well." Then she invited Taiyangzi to her secret room where she practiced Taoism. She entertained him with delicacies from land and sea and told him about how she practiced Yuzi's magic arts. Upon hearing this, Taiyangzi said, "We live in the same dynasty, drink the water under magic light, follow Yuzi's steps, and have the five elements in our bodies. All those who are able and virtuous and are of good character are intimate Taoist friends. It's not strange at all!"

Then Taiyangzi taught Taiyinnü ways to cultivate herself. Later, both of them became immortals.

From *Accounts of the Saints* • *Taiyinnü*

The Magic Finger

Taixuannü was originally called Zhuan He. When she was very young, her husband died. A fortune teller, after having examined her and her son's faces, said, "Neither you nor your son will live long." Upon hearing this, Taixuannü was determined to practice Taoism so as to prolong her life.

She began to learn Yuzi's magic arts. Soon she had a good command of them: She could keep her clothes dry after having entered water, and could walk on water in an unlined garment in the depths of winter for several days at a time, her skin remaining unchanged and her body staying warm.

Taixuannü had a magic finger. If she pointed at a locked door, cabinet or box with her finger, it would open by itself. If she pointed at a mountain with her finger, a landslide would take place, and if she pointed at a tree, it would wither. However if she pointed at something a second time it would be restored to its former state. She could also make a building disappear and appear again elsewhere just by point at it.

Taixuannü often went on trips with her disciples. At nightfall, Taixuannü would tap on a cliff with her stick. The rock would then split open, leading to a well-equipped house with a door, beds, furniture and food. So, no matter how far they roamed, they always felt at home.

Taixuannü was renowned for possessing 36 magical skills, with one of which she could revive dying people.

No one knew what Taixuannü ate every day, but whatever it was it made her younger and younger. Her hair never turned white. Later, she became an immortal.

From *Accounts of the Saints* • *Taixuannü*

Even Fowls and Dogs Go to Heaven

Prince Huainan (179-122 B.C.) of the Western Han Dynasty (206-24 B.C.) was the grandson of Emperor Gaozu, the founder of the dynasty. He longed to become an immortal, and was a patron of alchemists. One day, eight old men came to his residence. The doorkeeper said to them, "My master wishes to known the secret of eternal youth. You are so old and feeble; he will not want to meet you."

Thereupon, the eight made esoteric gestures, and suddenly changed into young men, full of life and vigor. Astonished, the doorkeeper took them to see Prince Huainan.

The latter greeted them warmly, and took them as his teachers.

One of Prince Huainan's subordinates, a man named Wu Bei, fell out of favor with his master. In fear of punishment, he secretly reported to Emperor Wu that Prince Huainan was planning to revolt. The eight immortals warned Prince Huainan of this, and told him that the only way to escape was to go to Heaven. Thereupon, they gave him and all his family a special concoction, after drinking which they all ascended to Heaven. Even the dogs and courtyard fowls which licked the bowl which had contained the elixir went up to Heaven.

This was reported to Emperor Wu, who then had Wu Bei executed. From then on Emperor Wudi also recruited alchemists, in a search for medicine which would prolong his life.

From *Accounts of the Saints* • *Prince Huainan*

Husband and Wife
Vie with Each Other

Madame Fan, wife of Liu Gang, began to learn Taoist arts in her childhood. Liu Gang, styled Bo Luan, once served as magistrate of Shangyu County (in present-day Zhejiang Province). He could write an official call to summon ghosts and gods, and understood the law of changes. But he kept all this secret from the people of his county. They did not know that the peaceful and prosperous lives they enjoyed were due to the magistrate's use of his special powers.

Often, when they sat at home idle, Liu Gang and his wife would compete with each other, using their magical skills. For instance, Liu Gang might set a distant barn on fire, whereupon his wife would douse the flames equally magically.

There were two peach trees in the courtyard of Liu Gang's residence. If the husband and wife each recited an incantation, the two trees would start to fight. Liu Gang's tree was never a match for Madame Fan's.

Liu Gang once spat on a plate. All of a sudden, his saliva turned into a carp. Madame Fan also spat on the plate, and her saliva become an otter, which swallowed the carp.

Liu Gang never won in competition with his wife.

From *Accounts of the Saints* • *Madame Fan*

Emperor Wen Receives Instructions

There was an old man called Mr. Heshang, whose original name is unknown. He lived alone in a thatched cottage by a river, where he devoted his life to the study of the Taoist classics. Emperor Wen of the Han Dynasty was also fascinated by the study of Taoism.

One day, he came across a passage in a Taoist text which he did not understand. He consulted his advisers, but not one could enlighten him. Finally, a courtier named Pei Kai told him about the hermit Heshang.

The emperor immediately dispatched someone to consult the wise man. But Heshang simply said, "Let he who wishes to consult the Tao come here in person." The emperor was indignant when he received this message, but went to Heshang's hut anyway. There, he upbraided the hermit, saying, "Everything on earth is subject to the emperor, for this is Heaven's decree."

Instead of replying, Heshang leapt into the air, and hovered some 30 m above the ground. From this vantage point, he lectured emperor Wen as follows: "I am neither in Heaven nor on earth; what then can Your Majesty do to make me subordinate to your commands?"

Realizing that the old man was an immortal, the emperor quickly alighted from his carriage, and humbly kowtowed. He then asked Heshang to instruct him in the principles of Taoism.

Seeing that Emperor Wendi was in great earnest, Mr. Heshang gave him a copy of *The Fundamental Text of Taoism* to the emperor, saying, "I have annotated this book for hundreds of years. You should study it carefully. You will find the answers to all your questions here. Over the past 1,700-odd years I have given copies of the book to only three other people. Please don't show it to anyone who should not read it."

Emperor Wendi knelt down, accepted the book and thanked the old man. Thereupon, Mr. Heshang vanished. The emperor had a high terrace built specially for offering sacrifices to the old man. Later, it was said that though Emperor Wendi was very interested in Taoist doctrines, he was not pious at heart. So Mr. Heshang displayed his magic powers to enlighten him so as to help him master the true essence of Taoism. As the old man's thatched cottage was by a river, he was named Mr. Heshang (on the river).

From *Accounts of the Saints* • *Mr. Heshang*

Mr. Kettle Finds a Disciple

During the Eastern Han Dynasty (25-220) there was a man called Mr. Kettle, whose original name is unknown. He left more than 20 volumes of *Mr. Kettle's Prescriptions* to posterity.

In Lunan (in present-day Henan Province), the superintendent of the local fair, a man named Fei Changfang, one day saw an old man come to the fair to sell medicines. The old man refused to bargain with anyone. All the medicines he sold worked well in curing various kinds of diseases. The old man could even predict how many days the patient would take to recover. Every day the old man gave most of his earnings to the local poor people leaving only a little bit for himself. He hung a kettle above the place where he sold his medicines, and at the end of the day he would jump into the kettle, when no one was looking. Only Fei Changfang, who paid great attention to him, knew that the old man was not an ordinary person.

Fei Changfang cleaned the ground in front of Mr. Kettle's stall and provided him with food every day. Mr. Kettle never thanked him, but Fei

Changfang gave no thought to this, continuing his humble ministrations.

One day, Mr. Kettle told Fei: "Come to me at dusk, when all the people have gone." Fei did as he was bidden. Mr. Kettle said, "Follow me into the kettle."

Fei Changfang jumped into the kettle, where he saw grand buildings with terraces, pavilions, towers, corridors and imposing doors. Mr. Kettle was waited on by dozens of servants.

Mr. Kettle told Fei: "I used to be an official in Heaven. But I made a mistake, and as a punishment, I was banished to earth. I observed you for a long time, and finally decided that you are an ideal candidate to learn some magic powers. I hope you will not mention this to anyone else. Now I intend to return to Fairyland. Would you like to go with me?"

"Of course," replied Fei. "But how can I explain my absence to my family?"

"That is easy," said Mr. Kettle.

He handed a bamboo stick to Fei Changfang and instructed him: "Pretend to be sick after you return home. Then put this bamboo stick in your bed. Then come back here."

When Fei Changfang returned, Mr. Kettle took him to a stone room to teach him the Taoist arts of healing. Many days passed, and finally it was time for Fei to leave. Again Mr. Kettle gave him a bamboo stick and said: "Ride on this and it will take you home."

Changfang said good-bye to Mr. Kettle and rode on the bamboo stick. In a minute he was back home.

Upon returning home, Fei Changfang began to treat patients. Not a single person he treated failed to recover.

From *Accounts of the Saints* • *Mr. Kettle*

Jie Xiang Shows off
His Magic Powers

Jie Xiang, styled Yuanze, was a native of Huiji (present-day Shaoxing in Zhejiang Province). A learned man, he was well versed in the *Book of Songs*, *Book of History*, *Book of Rites*, *Book of Changes* and *The Spring and Autumn Annals*. He was also well read in the fields of law, military arts, medicine, *yin* and *yang*, and novels, as well as having mastered the works of the philosophers. He cultivated himself according to Taoist doctrines, and once went to Mount Taishan to learn *qigong*. He had acquired some magic powers. For instance, he could bake a chicken without the fuel turning into ashes. He could stop all the families within a radius of one *li* cooking food, and all the fowls and dogs crowing and barking, and cause all the people at a fair to lose the ability to stand up. He could also turn himself into grass, a tree, a bird or an animal.

Jie Xiang was recommended to Sun Quan, the ruler of the State of Wu from 229 to 252. Sun Quan showed great respect for Jie Xiang, calling him Master Jie. He had a special residence built for him, and often bestowed presents on him. Sun Quan learnt magic arts from Jie Xiang. One skill he learned was how to leave and enter the palace without being detected by his bodyguards.

One day, Jie Xiang mentioned to Sun Quan that mullet was the tastiest of fish.

Sun Quan said, "The mullet lives in the sea, and it is very hard to catch it."

"It's not hard at all," Jie Xiang replied.

Jie Xiang had a pit dug in the palace, and filled it with water. He then took a fishing pole, and before long had caught a fine fat mullet. While the mullet was being cooked, Sun Quan sighed. "It's a pity that the envoy from the State of Shu has not come," he said. "He often brings us some ginger. Adding ginger to the fish would make it more delicious. Local ginger is no match for that from Shu."

"No problem," Jie Xiang said. "Just summon a messenger, and give him 5,000 coins." When this was done, Jie Xiang wrote a talisman, and tucked it into a cleft bamboo stick. He told the messenger: "Mount the stick and close your eyes. When the stick stops moving, open your eyes and buy ginger. Then ride the stick back here."

The messenger arrived in Chengdu, the capital of the State of Shu, in a moment. It so happened that Zhang Wen, an envoy from the State of Wu, was in Chengdu. One of Zhang Wen's attendants ran into the messenger just as the latter was buying ginger. The attendant was very surprised to see him there and asked him to deliver a letter to his home.

Jie Xiang asked Sun Quan time and time again to be allowed to leave the palace, but all in vain.

One day, Jie Xiang declared that he would fall ill on a certain day in a certain month in a certain year. On that very day, Sun Quan sent a palace maiden with a basket of pears to Jie Xiang. After eating one of the pears, Jie Xiang passed away. This was a grievous loss to Sun Quan.

From *Accounts of the Saints* • *Jie Xiang*

Rosin Saves Zhao Qu's Life

Long, long ago there was a man by the name of Zhao Qu, who lived in Shangdang (present-day Changzhi in Shanxi Province). He had suffered from boils for many years. He had consulted many doctors, but no one could cure him. When he was dying, his family removed him to a remote cave, and left him there with some food.

Zhao Qu felt very sad in the cave and cried bitterly for over a month. One day, an immortal happened to be passing by, and he asked Zhao Qu what had happened to him. Zhao Qu fell on his knees, told him everything and begged him to save him. The celestial then gave him a bag of medicine and taught him how to take it. After having taken the medicine for over a hundred days, Zhao Qu completely recovered, with rosy cheeks and a soft skin.

A few months later, the immortal came to see Zhao Qu again. Zhao Qu thanked him profusely, and asked him for the prescription for the wonderful medicine he had give him. The immortal then said, "It is just rosin. There is plenty of rosin on this mountain. After rosin is extracted and purified, it can help prolong people's lives." So saying, he disappeared.

Zhao Qu then left the cave, and returned home. His family was very astonished to see him, thinking he must be a ghost. Zhao Qu told them his story. From then on, he persisted in taking rosin. As time went by his body became lighter and lighter, and stronger and stronger. He could climb mountains and cross raging rivers all day long without feeling tired. At the age of over 170 he still looked young, with black hair and solid teeth. One night he saw a ring of light as big as a mirror in his bedroom. When he asked his sons and grandsons about it, they all denied that there was any such thing. Later, the ring of light became larger and larger, illuminating the house until it was as bright as daytime. Every night thereafter, Zhao Qu found two tiny beautiful girls on his face, each about two to three inches tall. The girls played games between Zhao Qu's nose and mouth. Later they grew up, and stayed behind to wait on Zhao Qu. He often heard melodious music and enjoyed it by himself. Later, he retired to Mount Baodu.

When the story spread that Zhao Qu had lived a long time because of taking rosin, many people tried to eat it. However, all of them stopped taking it after a month. It is really hard to find a man like Zhao Qu who can persist in eating rosin.

From *Baopuzi's Esoteric Affairs* • *Magic Medicine*

Anqi Sheng and Emperor Qin Shihuang

In the Qin Dynasty (221-206 B.C.), there was a man named Anqi Sheng who sold medicines by the sea. Several generations of the people of Langya (present-day Jiaonan County, Shandong Province) knew him. It was estimated that he was over a thousand years old. Later, Emperor Qin Shihuang invited him to the palace to have a chat with him. Their chat lasted three days and nights. The emperor was very surprised to learn that Anqi Sheng was so knowledgeable. He gave him a valuable gold screen as a present. Anqi Sheng put the gold screen in Fuxiang Pavilion. In return, he gave Emperor Qin Shihuang a pair of red jade boots, and left him a letter. In the letter he wrote: "Please come to the Penglai Fairyland to see me in a few thousand years' time."

When Anqi Sheng met Emperor Qin Shihuang, he was already over 1,000 years old. It was well known that the emperor was hot-tempered, arrogant, cruel, fierce and malicious. He did not believe in immortals, and could not tolerate those who held different opinions from his. Later, Emperor Qin Shihuang was determined to find the elixir of immortality, but was cheated by Lu Sheng and Xu Fu. During the three days and nights of their conversation, if Anqi Sheng had not been able to advance arguments to justify himself, he would have been executed by the emperor.

From *Baopuzi's Esoteric Affairs* • *Proper Words*

Walking on Water

Dong You, a native of Hailing (present-day Taizhou in Jiangsu Province), had two elder brothers. When he was very young, his father died. His mother was often worried that, as a poor and sick child, Dong You would not be able to support himself in the future. At the age of 18, Dong You said to his mother: "I am sick, and so I am afraid that I will be a drag on my two elder brothers. My life will not last long. I'd better become a Taoist and cultivate myself for the rest of my life." His mother agreed with him.

After becoming a Taoist, Dong You ate only vegetables, studied the scriptures and cultivated himself in accordance with Taoist doctrines. When he reached the age of 40, an immortal gave him a whip and taught him to walk on water by lashing the water with the whip.

In the Yixi reign period (405-418) of the Jin Dynasty, Dong You returned home, and took leave of his mother: "I have attained perfection in Taoism, and now I am going to Mount Emei. I don't know when I'll be back."

His mother watched him walk away on the surface of a nearby river, lashing it with his whip.

From *Accounts of Cave Immortals • Dong You*

Wang Zhi Watches a Game of Chess

Wang Zhi was a native of Dongyang (present-day Yiwu in Zhejiang Province). One day, he went to the mountains to cut firewood. He got lost, and could not find his way home. He found a cave, which he entered. After walking a long way, he came to an open space where two boys were playing chess. Wang Zhi was very fond of chess, so he put down his load of firewood, stuck his axe into a tree and watched the game with great interest. Noticing Wang Zhi standing there, one of the boys took a jujube out of his chest, gave it to Wang Zhi and told him to suck it. Wang Zhi did as he was bidden. Soon afterwards, the two boys finished playing chess. They said to Wang Zhi: "You have been here for a long time. You may go home now."

When Wang Zhi turned round to take his axe, he found that the axe head was buried deep in the tree trunk, and the wooden handle had rotted away. When he arrived home, he hardly recognized his hometown. Eventually he realized that he had spent several hundred years watching the chess game in the cave.

From *Accounts of Cave Immortals* • Wang Zhi

Long-Lasting Love

Chang Ji, a poor woodcutter, had a wise and able wife. One day when he was cutting firewood in the mountains he suffered an accident. At the news, his wife hurried to the mountains, weeping bitterly. A passer-by had pity on her, and gave her a triangular pot for decocting herbal medicine and a prescription. Before leaving, he told her: "After your husband takes the medicine, he will recover. If he persists in taking the medicine, he will be able to fly to Heaven."

Chang Ji's wife expressed her gratitude to him. Then she took her husband home. She waited on Chang Ji with care and administered the medicine. Soon Chang Ji was able to prepare the medicine for himself. He took it for a thousand days. By that time he was ready to fly. So, saying farewell to his wife, he flew away to the Penglai Fairyland.

Returning home, his wife felt lonely. Then she hit on the idea of preparing the medicine for herself.

Chang Ji's wife began to prepare medicine every day, and, like her husband, she persisted in drinking it for three years running.

She could finally fly too, and so she flew to the Penglai Fairyland to find her husband. When she did so, Chang Ji said, "I knew you would come."

From *Account of the Cave Immortals* • *Chang Ji*

The Story of Lan Caihe

During the Tang Dynasty (618-907) there was a man called Lan Caihe. No one knew where he came from. He wore a ragged garment all the year round, with a three-inch waistband, on which various kinds of ornaments were hung. On one of his feet he wore a boot, while the other foot was bare. In summer, he wore a purple garment under his blue robe, but he never sweated. In autumn even if he slept in the snow, his body gave out steam. When he went begging in the street, he often sang songs, to the accompaniment of a one-meter-long clapper.

After getting drunk, Lan Caihe would sing and dance in the street. He was always followed by crowds of people. When people asked him questions, Lan Caihe would answer them one by one with humorous language. Though he looked like a madman, he was actually very clever. When walking in the street, he often sang:

Lan Caihe sings a song.
How long will the world last?
Time flies quickly.
The ancients have gone,

And modern people come one after another.
Riding a phoenix to a green field in the
morning,
I see white waves of a plantation of mulberry
trees at dusk.
In the sky there is a beautiful scene
With gold and silver palaces of all shapes and
sizes.

He had a wide variety of songs. All of them mentioned a fairyland, which ordinary people could not understand. When people gave him coins, he would string them together, and trail them along behind him. He never turned back to look at them, and did not care if they were lost. Sometimes he would give the coins to poor people or leave them in wineshops.

He traveled round the country all the year round and remained young all the time. One day, when he was singing songs in Anhui, he heard music coming from a restaurant. He jumped up to the sky, rode the clouds, threw down his boot, blue robe, waistband and clapper, and flew away.

Lan Caihe was one of the legendary Eight Immortals. There are many stories about him.

From *Sequel to Accounts of the Saints*

Hou Daohua Becomes an Immortal

Many years ago, there was a man called Hou Daohua. He said he was from Mount Emei in Sichuan Province, and lived in the Yongle Taoist Temple in Hezhong (present-day Yongji County in Shanxi Province).

The Yongle Temple was often damaged by fierce winds. Hou Daohua, who was a skilled carpenter, would always repair it. Hou Daohua was hospitable to all the visitors to the temple, no matter whether they were Taoists or laymen. He fetched water for them, washed their clothes, and prepared and served food and tea. He did all the mis-cellaneous work in the temple, including cleaning the toilet and watering the vegetable garden. However, the more he did, the more the others looked down upon him. They treated Hou Daohua as a slave, and let him do everything for them.

Hou Daohua was an avid reader of books, and was steeped in the classics and history.

Whenever anybody asked him why he spent so much time reading, he would reply, "No one in heaven is ignorant; how can I become an immortal without reading books?"

This would cause a wave of laughter.

Over a decade passed, and a brilliant luster appeared on the beams of the Great Hall of the temple. Legend has it that during the Kaiyuan reign of the Tang Dynasty (713-741), Heavenly Master Liu once made pills of immortality in the temple. He first let a dog taste one, but the dog fell down dead. Thereupon Master Liu hid them on the beams. Many people did not believe the legend, and thought it was just a rumor.

One day, the Great Hall was slightly damaged in a storm. Hou Daohua climbed onto the beams to repair the roof. Suddenly he caught sight of a light. Following the light he found a box, inside which were two smaller ones. The smallest box was made of gold. He opened it and found a pill inside. Hou Daohua took out the pill, swallowed it and threw the box onto the ground. Nothing happened to him for the time being.

Then one day Hou Daohua got drunk at a fair and walked up to a huge pine tree in front of the temple. The tree was over a hundred years old. Hou Daohua climbed up it and began to chop its branches off with an axe.

The magistrate of Yongle County happened to be at the temple that day, and seeing Hou Daohua cutting off the branches from the magnificent pine tree, the magistrate cursed him in front of all the bystanders. Hou Daohua paid no attention to him.

Seven days later, Hou Daohua flew to Heaven.

From *Sequel to Accounts of the Saints*

Zhang Guolao Pretends
to Be Dead

During the Tang Dynasty (618-907) a man by the name of Zhang Guolao engaged in self-cultivation on Mount Zhongtiao near Changzhou. He often made trips to Shanxi Province. Old people claimed to have seen him when they were young, and at that time he said that he was already over a hundred years old.

Emperor Taizong (reigned 626-649) and Emperor Gaozong (reigned 650-683) of the Tang Dynasty invited him several times to the court, but Zhang Guolao declined.

In 690 Empress Wu Zetian came to power. She sent an official to summon Zhang Guolao. But Zhang pretended to be dead in front of the Dunü Temple. It was midsummer, and the weather was hot. The corpse soon became rotten. The official reported this to the empress, and all the officials and officers at the court believed that Zhang Guolao had died. To their surprise, someone saw him in the mountains near Changzhou.

In the 23rd year of the Kaiyuan reign period, Emperor Xuanzong (reigned 712-756) sent

Secretarial Receptionist Pei Wu to Changzhou to summon Zhang Guolao. At the first sight of Pei Wu, Zhang Guolao fell to the ground and died. Pei Wu, frightened, hurriedly set up an incense table, burned joss sticks and candles, and read the emperor's decree. Soon afterwards Zhang Guolao revived. Pei Wu dared not use force against Zhang Guolao, so he hastily returned to the court to report to the emperor. Emperor Xuanzong then sent another official, Xu Jiao, to invite Zhang Guolao to the capital.

Zhang Guolao followed Xu Jiao to Luoyang, the Eastern Capital, and stayed at the Hall for Virtuous People. Soon afterwards, he was taken to the palace in a sedan chair. Emperor Xuanzong treated him as an honored guest. Princes, dukes and ministers showed him great respect. But when they asked him about the immortals, he put them off with vague answers.

"I was born in the year Bingzi, during the reign of Emperor Yao. I don't know how long I have lived," Zhang Guolao replied. "I served as an official under Emperor Yao. As I am good at practicing self-cultivation, I can live without eating any food for a long time, but I have to drink wine."

On hearing this, Emperor Xuanzong invited Zhang Guolao to stay in the inner palace, and granted him a ration of wine.

Zhang Guolao declined. "I'm not a heavy drinker," he said. "But one of my disciples is a good drinker."

Emperor Xuanzong let Zhang Guolao summon his disciple. Soon a young Taoist priest flew down from the eaves. About 16 years old, the young man was handsome, refined, courteous and well spoken. The emperor invited him to sit down. But Zhang Guolao said, "My disciple should stand beside me. It is inappropriate to let him sit down."

Emperor Xuanzong, who was very fond of the young Taoist priest, gave him wine. The young man was such a good drinker that he did not get drunk even after having drunk an enormous amount of wine.

"Don't give him any more wine, Your Majesty," Zhang Guolao said. "Otherwise he will make a fool of himself."

The emperor did not take his advice, but gave more wine to the young Taoist priest. To his surprise wine suddenly gushed out from the top of his head onto the ground and turned into a gold wine container. The emperor and his consorts burst into laughing. They examined the wine container, and found that it came from the Hall for Virtuous People.

Zhang Guolao displayed a wide variety of his magic powers. Emperor Xuanzong issued a decree: "Mr. Zhang Guolao from Changzhou is a man who often roams in Fairyland. He has immortal magic powers, and has attained a lofty realm of thought. It is my good fortune to have been able to summon him to the capital. We do not know how many years he has lived. It is said that he was born in the era of Fu Xi (3,000 years B.C.). According to the principle of recruiting able and virtuous people, I shall appoint him Grand Master of Splendid Happiness, with the name Mr. Tongxuan."

But Zhang Guolao protested, "I am old and feeble; please allow me to return to Changzhou."

Zhang Guolao was also one of the legendary Eight Immortals. There are many stories about him.

From *Sequel to Accounts of the Saints*

Li Yuan Leaves Mount Huashan

During the reign of Emperor Xuanzong (reigned 712-756), a man by the name of Li Yuan lived at the foot of Mount Huashan, eating only medicinal herbs. He loved drinking wine with his neighbors.

One day, Li Yuan, riding a white deer, waved to his neighbors, saying, "Good-bye, I'm going to Mount Tiantai." Three old men stood in the road, trying to stop him. They said, "Mr. Li, you get along well with the local people; why do you want to leave us so suddenly?" "My old friends," Li Yuan replied, "when people get close to each other, they will surely be separated. This is a law of Nature. I don't dare run counter to the law; so I must leave."

"You are used to eating medicinal herbs growing on Mount Huashan. What will you eat when you are at Mount Tiantai," the three old men asked him.

"There are medicinal herbs there, too," Li Yuan answered.

Finding that Li Yuan had made up his mind, the three old men sat down on straw cushions, poured out some home-made wine for him, and said a few parting words. When Li Yuan took his leave, he left three pills with the old men and urged them to take one each right away. Then he left on the white deer.

Later, two of the three old men, who took the pills, on the spot, lived to the age of 150. The remaining one, who did not take his pill, died only a few months later. Hence, the local people believed that Li Yuan was an immortal.

From *Strange Stories of Immortals*

The Old Medicine Seller

In Puzhou (present-day Yongze County in Shanxi), there was an old man who sold medicine in the market. No one knew his name, so everyone called him the medicine seller.

Wang Yu, a local rich man, was reserved, kind-hearted and skilled at medical treatment. He invited the medicine seller to dinner, one evening, hoping to learn something from him. But when the old man arrived, instead of saluting the host, he bowed to Wang Yu's servant. Wang Yu did not take this to heart, but presented a cup of wine to the drug seller in person. The old man laughed, took the cup and drank the wine in one gulp. Then he turned to Wang Yu and said, "What do you want to ask me? Don't stand on ceremony."

"You never tell people what your name is. Could you please tell me who you are?" Wang Yu asked.

The medicine seller replied, "My feet are on the ground, with the sky above my head. I get *qi* (vital energy) from Heaven and Earth. As a man, my surname is 'man.' So is my first name. I don't need any other name."

"The medicines you sell can cure various diseases. What is in them?" Wang Yu asked again.

"There are no various diseases. All people suffer from the same disease. Man survives by relying on *qi*. If *qi* goes through the body smoothly, one will be in a good health; otherwise, one will be sick. Hence there is only one disease in the world. I don't think it is necessary to give diseases various names. I only sell one kind of medicine; because I think all diseases are produced by one cause, and need only one type of medicine to cure them."

"Why do you refuse to sell your medicine to some patients?" Wang Yu asked.

The old man kept silent.

"Could you please take my servant as your disciple?" Wang Yu asked.

"Your servant has the same status as I have. If you give me your servant, I shall give you a book in return," the old man said.

Wang Yu nodded in agreement. He received a book from the old man, and let his servant go with him. The servant was very glad at this. Soon the old man and his disciple went away, and no one knew where they went.

After having read the book given to him by the medicine seller, Wang Yu made great progress in his medical pursuits. One day, a person came and insisted on seeing the book. When Wang Yu showed it to him, the man and the book both disappeared.

From *Strange Stories of Immortals*

Taking a Tour Riding a Dog

A man by the name of Ge Yong often took a yellow dog with him walking in the Qishan and Longshan mountains. He was fond of chatting with monks and Taoist priests, with whom he often chatted until midnight. Then Ge Yong would sleep in the open.

A man named Wang Feng had great respect for Ge Yong. One day, Ge Yong said to Wang Feng: "Let's take a tour riding on my dog."

"Can we ride on your dog?" Wang Feng asked dubiously.

"Sure," Ge Yong replied.

The two men thereupon mounted the dog. No sooner had they done so than the yellow dog jumped up from the ground and began to fly in the air. In no time at all, they came to a mountain thousands of miles away. The mountain had elegant peaks and picturesque scenery, totally different from any scene on earth. Hand in hand, Ge Yong and Wang Feng entered a cave, where there were rare trees and flowers, graceful pavilions, high terraces and clear streams. They came to a grand mansion, from which three beautiful women came out to greet them. Following them, the two men climbed a tower. The women lifted a pearl curtain, put out a jade table and chairs, and invited them to drink wine. During the dinner the women played the *sheng* (a reed pipe wind instrument) and the *xiao* (a vertical bamboo flute). Ge Yong said to Wang Feng: "These three ladies are all immortals. They seldom come to meet here. I knew that beforehand, so I invited you to come here with me. Now we should go home; otherwise, they will not feel free to play their games."

Then Ge Yong walked out of the cave with Wang Feng. The three women saw them off at the entrance of the cave. Saying, "I'll see you next year," Ge Yong went back to the Qilong Mountains with Wang Feng on the yellow dog. But three years had already past. Ge Yong said to Wang Feng: "I'm going to take a trip to the east. You stay here." So saying, Ge Yong disappeared, and never returned.

From *Strange Stories of Immortals*

The Girl Who Wanted to Learn Taoist Magic

In Xichuan (present-day Chengdu in Sichuan) there was a rich man named Peng Zhiwei. He had a daughter who was fascinated by magic. She once told her father that she planned to read Taoist books and cultivate herself according to Taoist doctrines. Peng Zhiwei firmly opposed this.

When his daughter was 16, a boy on a white crane came to Peng Zhiwei's home and said to his daughter: "I'm a Taoist. I hear that you are interested in Taoist magic, so I have come here to teach you."

Surprised and happy, the girl hid the boy and white crane. A few days later, a maid got to know about this and warned the girl that her father would be angry if he found out.

"Please keep the secret for me for the time being," the girl begged the maid. "I'll let him leave after having learned Taoist magic from him."

At midnight one night, the girl said to the boy: "To learn Taoism, one must read Taoist books. However, my father prevents me from doing so. What can I do?"

The boy replied: "You love Taoism with great sincerity. So there is no difference between you and those who cultivate their conduct according to the Taoist doctrines. Since ancient times, those flying to the sky in the daytime have never read Taoist books. They are born Taoists. The Queen Mother of the West once said Emperor Wudi of the Han Dynasty was a born immortal."

"I wear clothes and eat food like ordinary people; it will be very difficult for me to become an immortal," the girl said.

"If you admire the immortal ways from the bottom of your heart, and concentrate on them, the immortals will be moved. Those who always remain undecided will never become celestials," the boy explained.

The girl then asked, "How will you teach me then?"

"You're not an ordinary girl," he replied. "If you have made up your mind, you'll go to Heaven pretty soon." So saying, the boy stood up and took his leave. "I've told you about the immortal ways," he said. "I hope you will concentrate on cultivating yourself. I'm leaving now."

Then the boy flew away on the crane.

From *Strange Stories of Immortals*

The Magic Pond

Dongfang Xuan, a native of Jingzhou, lived in a thatched cottage at the foot of South Mountain. Both he and his wife were good at Taoist magic. One day, when a Taoist passed their home, they invited him in. Dongfang Xuan prepared dainties fruit by peeling a bamboo pole, and wine by fetching spring water. The Taoist was very surprised at this. Then the wife shouted at another bamboo pole, which turned into a large bird. The woman mounted the bird and flew away. In a moment she came back, bringing a chessboard with her. She said to the Taoist: "I will play chess with Dongfang Xuan."

"Where did you get this chessboard?" the Taoist asked.

"I got it from a friend who lives by the South China Sea," Dongfang Xuan's wife replied.

"Who is your friend?"

"My friend also has magic powers. She often comes to visit me. She will come today."

"How did you learn magic powers?" the Taoist asked Dongfang Xuan.

Dongfang Xuan replied, "Long ago, I met a lady

whose surname is Fan. I married her. She taught me magic arts, but I don't know where she learnt the magic."

While the Taoist was chatting with Dongfang Xuan, the sound of music was heard. Raising his head, the Taoist saw a pretty girl falling from the sky. She asked Dongfang Xuan's wife with a smile: "Why do you invite an ordinary person again?"

"This Taoist was just passing, so I invited him to be my guest. He is different from Dongfang Xuan."

"Why haven't you begun playing chess?" the girl asked.

"You two may play by yourselves; I'll talk to the guest," Dongfang Xuan replied.

The girl draw a circle on the ground. All of a sudden, the circle turned into a big pond surrounded by tall pine trees and green bamboos. Lotus flowers clustered by the banks of the pond, among which there was a colorful boat. The girl jumped into the boat. Dongfang Xuan's wife threw an embroidered shoe into the pond, and it turned into a boat. The two women sang as they floated in the boats. Their songs were very sad. The Taoist was moved and said, with tears in his eyes: "I have cultivated myself according to the Taoist doctrines for 15 years, and have left my footprints in many places, but I have never met anybody as capable as those two women."

Upon hearing this, the two women went ashore,

looking unhappy. They stared at each other for a long time. Then the girl shouted at the pond, and the pond, lotus flowers and boats disappeared in the twinkling of any eye. Then the two women left, each riding on a pole. Dongfang Xuan smiled, and said to the Taoist: "Master, you had better leave right now. Don't stay here any longer."

The Taoist stood up and took his leave. The following year, when the Taoist passed South Mountain again, he went to pay a visit to Dongfang Xuan. But he was told that Dongfang Xuan and his family had moved away.

From *Strange Stories of Immortals*

Traveling on a Tortoise

A man by the name of Li Yang lived in central Sichuan. He had cultivated himself according to the Taoist doctrines for more than 10 years. One day, Li Yang came across a large tortoise by a river, which was as white as jade. Li Yang took it home.

Three years passed, and one day the tortoise left traveling on the wind, and came back seven days later. Puzzled, Li Yang said: "Taoism is a mystery. It is very hard to master it. Long ago I heard about the 'Three-Purities' Fairyland. I made painstaking efforts to cultivate myself for over 10 years, but I saw no sacred traces to give me hope. Then I discovered the white tortoise by the river." He then addressed the tortoise: "Why did you leave me a few days ago, then return? If you're an immortal tortoise, you may leave, and then come back. If you're not an immortal tortoise, you may leave and not come back." The tortoise suddenly soared into the sky, returning after seven days.

Li Yang believed that the tortoise was an immortal. One day when he was walking by the river with the tortoise, when an old man came up, and said to Li Yang: "This tortoise is mine. I lost it a long time ago. Where did you get it?"

"I picked it up by the river," Li Yang replied.

"This tortoise can travel in the sky and under water. Riding on its back, you can journey to anywhere you want to go. Since you have raised it for quite a long time, I will give it to you as a gift. You may visit Fairyland by riding on it. It will take you to the ends of Heaven and Earth."

Li Yang bowed to the old man to express his gratitude.

When he raised his head, he found that the stranger had vanished. Then Li Yang put one foot on the tortoise, which grew bigger and bigger until it was as large as an ox. Li Yang mounted it. The tortoise then headed for the river, the waters of which parted before it. Suddenly, it soared into the sky. After they had traveled for several days and covered about 5,000 km, Li Yang, who was frightened by this time, begged the tortoise: "Please take me back home." In a moment Li Yang found himself back at home.

Knowing that the tortoise had magic powers, Li Yang took another trip, this time to the west, on it. A few days later, they came to a mountain where there were jade trees and a jade pond. There was someone singing at the top of the mountain. Again, Li Yang asked the tortoise to take him home. Another time, he mounted the tortoise and went eastward. They came to a large river, stretching to the horizon. In the river there were mountains with towering buildings and elegant pavilions. Seeing it, Li Yang was frightened and asked the tortoise to take him home.

Hearing about these adventures, the people of Sichuan said that Li Yang should have stayed in Fairyland. One person made a special trip to Li Yang's home, and asked him about it. Li Yang replied, "I spend most of my time in the mountains, gathering medicinal herbs." When the visitor asked Li Yang about the tortoise, he said, "I found it by the river. Though it is a strange color, it does not look any different from other tortoises." That very night, the visitor stole the tortoise. Later Li Yang left home to take a trip, and no one knew where he went.

From *Strange Stories of Immortals*

Guan Ge Teaches Zhang Guolao a Lesson

Guan Ge was a native of the State of Zhao (in present-day Hebei Province). In his early youth he was keen on Taoism, and did not like farming. He often traveled between Zhao and the State of Wei (in present-day Henan Province). He cared nothing for modesty and courtesy, but was very good at speaking. One day, he ran into Zhang Guolao. The latter waved to him, and said, "Come here, Guan Ge."

"Who are you?" said Guan Ge.

"I'm Zhang Guolao."

"Zhang Guolao, what do you want with me?"

Zhang Guolao, who was very unhappy to hear Guan Ge address him disrespectfully by name, said to Guan Ge: "Don't you know courtesy? Even the emperor has great respect for me. How dare you be rude to me?"

"I'm not an emperor. Why should I respect you?"

Zhang Guolao invited Guan Ge to go to Mount Hengshan with him, and Guan Ge agreed. When

Zhang Guolao asked Guan Ge to close his eyes, Guan Ge said: "Can't I visit Mount Hengshan without closing my eyes?"

"You're an ordinary person," Zhang Guolao answered.

"You're also an ordinary person. Why don't you close your eyes?" Guan Ge retorted.

Zhang Guolao threw his stick into the sky, and it immediately turned into an ox. Zhang Guolao then let Guan Ge mount the ox. They climbed to the top of the mountain and sat down.

Zhang Guolao said to Guan Ge: "You have observed the bustling world, the worries of ordinary people, the changes of the seasons and the passage of time. Why do you only travel between the states of Zhao and Wei instead of going further afield? These two states are battlefields; they are not suitable for Taoists. If you want to get rid of your worries, you must purify your heart. The states of Zhao and Wei are not places for you to get rid of your worries."

Guan Ge replied, "As a Taoist, I should not only go to special places. It makes no difference to me if I travel between Zhao and Wei or visit the Yuqing or Penglai fairylands. If you think the emperor should be respectful to you, while I, an ordinary person, should be humble, and you may address me disrespectfully by name, it seems as if you were in Yuqing and Penglai in the morning, and in Zhao or Wei in the evening. So why should I take a long trip? I think you should be off to distant parts so as to avoid all the things in the world. Otherwise you will die on earth. You must not be like me."

Zhang Guolao smiled, but said nothing. Guan Ge continued, "Did you try to show me how to turn a stick into an ox when you invited me to take a tour of Mount Hengshan? Don't you know that everything in the world is changeable. It is not strange that a thing can be changed into something else, and human beings can become immortals."

So saying, Guan Ge stood up and left without saying good-bye to Zhang Guolao. He built a thatched cottage on the mountain and lived there. Later, he was seen in the Jishan Mountains.

From *Strange Stories of Immortals*

Abandoned by Immortals

A man by the name of Ding Shi frequently visited Luoyang. He said that he was a hermit on Mount Songshan. Someone asked him: "You're about a hundred years old. When did you start to live in seclusion on Mount Songshan?"

Ding Shi replied, "I was a Confucianist when Emperor Qin Shihuang was in power. But when Prime Minister Li Si proposed that all historical records in the imperial archives be burnt and all Confucianists be killed, I escaped to Mount Songshan, where I met an old man. He said to me: 'I can enable you to live a long life.' Then he gave me a pill. I took the pill and have lived until today. Though my hair is white, my appearance remains unchanged. I can't remember how many years I have lived. I knew Dongfang Shuo of the Han Dynasty. He used to be a servant of an immortal. But he was very unruly, and so he was driven out of the Fairyland. Once I went to see the Queen Mother. She told me all about it. Then I asked Dongfang Shuo about it. Dongfang Shuo smiled and admitted it. I also knew Liu Chen and Ruan Zhao, both laymen. Once they entered the Peach Blossom

Immortal's Cave by mistake. However, they could not forget their lives on earth, so they could not become immortals. Later, most immortals flew to Heaven during the daytime; but they could not come back. As I'm not an immortal, I cannot often meet them."

"But you have taken the pill of immortality; why can't you become an immortal?"

Ding Shi replied, "Though I can live a long life, I don't know how to fly to Heaven."

Ding Shi made it a rule that he pay a visit to Luoyang every spring. He had been to the city dozens of times, so lots of people in Luoyang knew him. When An Lushan rose in rebellion (755-763), Ding Shi told some people in Luoyang: "I must flee from a calamity. The non-Han ethnic groups living in the north and west in ancient times are different from the Confucianists." Then Ding Shi left, and never returned to Luoyang. The people believed that he was a god of the land.

From *Strange Stories of Immortals*

A Scholar and a Goddess

A man by the name of Ren Sheng lived as a hermit on Mount Songshan, where he devoted himself to reading books. Though he had lofty aspirations and interests, Ren Sheng preferred a quiet life. Living on Mount Songshan in seclusion, he could smell some queer fragrance every night.

One night, he heard someone outside the door address him: "I am destined to be your wife. I have been waiting here for quite a long time."

Thinking she was a mountain spirit, Ren Sheng refused to admit her. However, the person walked in. It was a young lady. She was very beautiful, and was accompanied by two maids. Without saying a word, the girl picked up a brush and wrote a poem on a piece of paper:

I belong to Heaven,
But I have come to the earth today.
As you are free from care on earth,
I come here to suggest that you practice Taoism.

The young lady then left, together with her maids. Ren Sheng went over to pick up the paper, finding that her handwriting was graceful. Ren

Sheng was more suspicious than ever that she was a ghost or some other kind of spirit.

Three days later the lady came again. But the scholar was so strong-willed that he was not lured by her. "I'm not a mountain spirit nor a wood demon," said the lady. "My name is listed in the heavenly register of names. I am destined to look for my husband on earth. Finding that you have eschewed fame and wealth, I am willing to be your wife to help you prolong your life and remove hidden disasters. However I am unlucky that you refuse to accept me as your wife." Then she wrote another poem, and left. It read:

Ge Hong (a famous Taoist) has a wife;
And the Queen Mother has a husband.
Even immortals need to get married.
What about you?

Ren Sheng sat facing the wall, and ignored the lady. She then wrote another poem:

Since you refuse to come to your sense,
I don't need to express my feelings to you.
When next spring comes,
We'll go to Fairyland by boat.

She signed the poem, turned round, walked out of the door, and flew away.

A few days later, a friend of Ren Sheng's came. Ren Sheng showed the three poems written by the lady to his friend. His friend scolded him for not recognizing a real goddess.

217

Several months later, Ren Sheng fell seriously ill. A lady by the name of Sansuyuanjun treated him. After he recovered, he found out that Sansuyuanjun was none other than the goddess who had visited him before.

From *Strange Stories of Immortals*

Lü Dongbin Becomes an Immortal

Lü Shaoguang, a successful candidate in the imperial examination at the provincial level, failed in the highest imperial examination time and time again. Disheartened, he was determined to go on trips to famous mountains and rivers. One day, on his way to Chang'an (present-day Xi'an), he passed by a mountain stream and saw an immortal writing a poem on a cliff:

> Holding a wine pot while sitting or lying,
> I don't care about anything in the Eastern
>   Capital.
> Without a name in the world,
> I live a carefree life on earth.

After reading the poem, Shaoguang fell down on his knees and asked him for instructions. The immortal let Shaoguang compose a poem to express his determination. Then Shaoguang recited a poem:

> I was born into a Confucianist's family,
> Wearing cloth robes with tassels and a belt.
> Others seek fame and gain in the world,
> While I am waiting to be summoned to Heaven.

The immortal was pleased with this poem. Knowing that Shaoguang understood Taoism well, he said to him:

"I live in a cave on the summit of South Mountain. You may come with me." Then the immortal held Shaoguang by the hand, stepped on clouds and flew to the cave, where there was a myriad of sun rays and three tigers at the entrance. The immortal shouted at them, and the tigers ran off down the mountain. After entering the cave, the immortal invited Shaoguang to sit on a rock stool. Soon a young boy in green clothes came out with some wine. When they were drinking, the boy came in to report that immortals from the Penglai Fairyland had invited the immortal to the banquet. The immortal did not dare to delay. Before his departure, the immortal said, "If you are determined to cultivate yourself according to the Taoist doctrines, you should change your name to Lü Yan and style yourself Lü Dongbin."

Then Lü Yan stayed in the cave reading the books preserved in the cave day and night. One day, when the immortal asked him if he missed home, Lü Yan replied, "I've broken off relations with the mortal life. I'm so fortunate to have your instructions. Now I have understood Taoism. How dare I miss the worldly life?" The immortal was overjoyed at this speech. Lü Yan asked:

"What is an immortal?"

The immortal replied, "You should know that

yin is soul and *yang* is spirit. If a man can combine *yin* with *yang*, or his soul with his spirit, he will become an immortal."

Lü Yan sighed and said, "It is very hard to understand."

At this moment, a servant boy came to report that two Taoists had come to see the Immortal Zhongli. Then Lü Yan realized that his master was none other than the Immortal Han Zhongli. Zhongli invited the two Taoists into the cave and introduced Lü Dongbin to them: "This is Lü Yan, also known as Lü Dongbin." Seeing Lü Yan had delicate features and a lofty spirit, Immortal Zheng asked, "Could you please compose a poem since you have left the vanity of the world?"

Lü Yan recited a poem right away:

> *After many transmigrations I have come to this life.*
> *In this life my body has become very light.*
> *I left my home and stay in the mountains,*
> *To cultivate myself according to Taoist doctrines.*

The three immortals spoke highly of this poem, saying that Lü Dongbin would become an immortal himself soon.

One of the immortals told Lü Dongbin: "You should not stay in the cave long. In 10 years' time we shall meet at Lake Dongting."

So saying, Han Zhongli picked up a brush and wrote a poem on the wall of the cave:

> *During the daytime the sun is bright;*
> *And at night the moon is round and clear.*
> *After the combination of* yin *and* yang, *soul and spirit,*
> *One may go up to Heaven.*

Then Han Zhongli threw the brush away. Lü Yan was also known as Lü Chunyang.

Lü Dongbin was also one of the Eight Immortals. There are many stories about Lü Dongbin.

From *Strange Stories of Immortals*

Azaleas Bloom in Autumn

During the Tang Dynasty, when Zhou Bao served as the supply commissioner for Western Zhejiang, a Taoist often came to the town where he lived to sell medicines. The Taoist was named Yin Tianxiang and styled Qiqi. The local people called him Qiqi.

This man was a skilled medical practitioner. One year, when Western Zhejiang was attacked by a pestilence, Qiqi prepared some medicines himself and all the patients who took his medicines soon recovered. Zhou Bao was very grateful to Qiqi; he showed him great respect and treated him as his honored guest. Qiqi did not cultivate himself very often; instead he was very fond of drinking wine.

Soon after the Mid-Autumn Festival, Zhou Bao was drinking wine with Qiqi and some of his colleagues. Seeing that Zhou Bao was laden with anxieties, one of his colleagues asked him the reason. Zhou Bao shook his head and did not answer. After the wine had gone round three times, Qiqi suddenly began to sing, while beating time on the table:

Wine can be made right away,
And flowers can blossom in no time.
Jade changes color when I play the qin.
With a stove I can make white pills of
   immortality.

Zhou Bao was surprised at this. He had not known before that Qiqi had such great magic powers. Lightheartedly, Zhou Bao asked: "Is it true that you can make flowers blossom right away?"

"Of course," Qiqi replied with a smile. "I can show you right now."

Zhou Bao told a servant boy to bring out a pot with withered flowers in it, and put it on a table. Qiqi sprinkled some wine on the withered flowers. All of a sudden, buds sprang from the branches, and the flowers came into full bloom. Everyone burst into applause.

Zhou Bao kneeled on the ground and asked Qiqi, "Are you really an immortal?"

Qiqi helped him up and let him take his seat.

What was Zhou Bao's worry? It turned out that not far from the town stood the Gulin Temple, where rare flowers were in full bloom all the year round. Of them there was an azalea plant, over three meters tall. At the end of every spring, the azaleas were very bright. The abbot of the temple said that the plant was originally planted and raised by a foreign monk with some special concoction. Later, when it was moved to the temple, it was locked in a garden to prevent it from being damaged. When the azaleas were in bloom, the door of the garden would be opened for special guests to appreciate them. Anyone who picked a flower would die or fall ill for sure. Someone said that in the garden a girl in red garments could often be seen moving around the flowers. At the slightest sound, she would leave right away. Upon hearing this, Zhou Bao went with his colleagues to view the azaleas. The flowers were so beautiful that Zhou Bao wrote a poem upon returning home in praise of them. So did his colleagues. Their poems were spread far and wide, and as a result, a continuous stream of visitors came to the temple. All the people in the city, men and women, old and young, flocked to the temple, ignoring their own work. Zhou Bao, who had no idea how to handle the situation was very worried.

"The flowers in the Gulin Temple are one of the earth's wonders. However, the local people show so much interest in them that they ignore their own business. It is a big problem," Zhou Bao murmured.

"Don't worry about it, sir. The flowers will fall pretty soon," Qiqi said.

"Really? What a pity!" Zhou Bao was sorry to hear it.

"The flowers are quite unusual. They do not curry favor with high officials and noble lords, but treat all folks equally. They are as lofty and precious as the peonies raised by Empress Wu

225

Zetian. However, I'm afraid they will not last long," Qiqi said.

"Then we shall no longer see these beautiful azaleas in the future, you mean?" Zhou Bao asked.

Qiqi was silent for a while. Then he said, "I told you I can make flowers boom instantly. I mean what I say. By the way, what is the date today?"

"It will soon be the Double Ninth Festival (ninth day of the ninth lunar month)," one of Zhou Bao's colleagues said.

"The azaleas come into bloom in spring," said Qiqi. It is autumn now, and their bloom has faded. I hope all of you will go to the temple on the Double Ninth Festival to see the azaleas for the last time." So saying Qiqi stood up and took his leave.

The following day was the fifth day of the ninth lunar month. Qiqi went on a tour of the mountain during the daytime, and put up at the temple for the night. He stayed at the temple for the next two days. On the night of the eighth day of the ninth month Qiqi was pacing back and forth in the garden. At about midnight the girl in red garments came. At the sight of Qiqi, she said angrily: "You plan to let the azaleas bloom for Zhou Bao and his friends. It is against the will of Heaven, you know!"

"Who are you?" said Qiqi.

"I have guarded the azaleas for a hundred years at the order of Heaven. Soon I'll return to the Heaven." With this, the girl disappeared.

The following day, Zhou Bao and his colleagues

226

came to the temple and told the monks their intention. The abbot protested that the azaleas had withered, and there were no flowers for them to appreciate. Zhou Bao nevertheless insisted on entering the garden, and sure enough the azaleas were in full bloom. All the people were overjoyed to hear this and flocked to the temple as usual. They stayed in the garden to appreciate the flowers the whole day, not leaving until sunset.

A few days later a monk got up early in the morning, and found all flowers gone, without leaving any fallen petals. After that, the azaleas never came into bloom there again. Two years later, during the rebellion started by Xue Xuan and Liu Hao, the Gulin Temple was burnt down, and the garden was left in ruins.

From *Sequel to Accounts of the Saints*

A Boat Ride on a Map

Chen Jiqing, a native of Southeast China, had tarried in the capital for 10 years, waiting to take the imperial examination. He felt ashamed to go home, for he had sworn that he would not return until he had accomplished something of consequence.

One day he went to the Black Dragon Temple to visit the abbot. It happened that the abbot was out, so Chen decided to wait in the inner room. As he lifted the door curtain, he found an old man already waiting by the fireplace who introduced himself as a hermit from South Mountain.

The inner room was quiet. On the wall of the room was a map of the country. To kill time, Chen Jiqing traced the route with his fingertip to his home town. He sighed and said, "If I could actually sail down these rivers by boat to my home, it would be the accomplishment of a lifetime."

Upon hearing this, the hermit felt sympathy for Chen. He walked out of the room, and picked a bamboo leaf from the courtyard and folded it into the shape of a boat. He placed the boat on the map and said to Chen Jiqing: "Now concentrate your mind and keep your eyes fixed on this boat, and you'll be able to fulfill your life-long wish."

After staring at the boat for a while, Chen felt that waves were rising on the Weishui River and the leaf-boat had expanded. A sail was hoisted and he found himself stepping aboard the boat, which set sail, floating down the river. On his way he stopped over at scenic spots and historical sites, and paid visits to famous temples, leaving poems here and there on the walls.

He reached home in about 10 days. His wife, brother and children welcomed him happily after their long separation. Two days passed, and Chen Jiqing said to his wife: "The date set for the imperial examination is drawing near. I cannot stay, but must return tonight."

Before Chen boarded his leaf-boat, he wrote a poem on the wall of his study:

Drinking wine I become more worried,
And I compose a poem with tears in my eyes.

The leaf-boat retraced its route upstream back to the Weishui River, and soon arrived at Chang'an. Once off the boat, he went by sedan chair to the Black Dragon Temple. There he saw the hermit sitting by the fireplace with a shaggy cape tightly wrapped round his shoulders. Chen Jiqing went over to bow to the hermit, and asked, "Wasn't all that a mere dream?"

"You'll be able to decide for yourself later," replied the hermit with a smile.

A few months later, Chen's family sent a servant to Chang'an. The servant mentioned his visit to his home, and showed him the verse he left on the wall of his study, which his wife had copied down for him. Only then did he believe that what he had experienced was not a dream.

Making Pills of Immortality

Liu Wuming lived in Chengdu. Legend has it that he was a descendant of Liu Bei, Emperor Zhaolie of the State of Shu during the Three Kingdoms Period (220-280). From his childhood he showed signs of being very intelligent. One day a Taoist passed by his home. Seeing Liu Wuming, the Taoist said, "If this boy cultivates himself according to the Taoist doctrines, he will live forever."

When Liu Wuming grew up he was more interested in Taoism than in fame and wealth. He devoted himself to reading the works of Lao Zi and Zhuang Zi, cultivating his conduct and picking medicinal herbs to prepare pills of immortality.

In spite of many experiments, he failed to find the formula for making the pills. So he decided to leave home to look for an eminent teacher.

One day he climbed Mount Qingcheng (present-day Mount Tiangu in the southwest of Guanxian County, Sichuan Province) and found a cave on the northern side. After having walked for a great distance in the cave, he came to an open area, where he saw an old man with a graceful bearing. Liu Wuming fell to his knees, and asked for instructions.

The old man pointed at a room in the rock face, and told Liu Wuming to stay in the room, abstaining from meat and cultivating himself so as to show his sincerity.

Liu Wuming did as he was bidden. Seven days later, the old man taught him the secret of making magic elixirs.

The old man said, "The elixirs can be divided into three kinds, primary, secondary and highest grade. They are mainly made of lead and mercury, plus some other minerals. The combination of lead and mercury will become light water after being smelted for several days; purple powder for another seven days; and ashes in five colors for another seven days. Then the ashes are refined for another two years to make a primary elixir. One who takes primary elixir may prolong his life and turn his white hair black. One who keeps taking primary elixir for three years running will be able to roam among high mountains and over turbulent seas. If a god of the land takes a primary elixir, he will be able to come and go as he wishes, ride a flying dragon and undergo various transformations. Primary elixirs become secondary elixirs after being refined for 16 solar terms. High-grade elixirs are made from a mixture of secondary elixirs, the five metals, lead, mercury and some special minerals, and refined for 1,000 days."

The true man continued, "The prepared elixirs should be well preserved and should not be shown to others rashly. Only show them to people accomplished in the ways of Taoism."

Liu Wuming took the old man's words to heart. He said good-bye to the immortal, and went to the mountains to cultivate himself.

From *Stories Excluded from the Accounts of the Saints*

A Golden Millet Dream

Legend has it that during the Huichang reign period (841-846) of Emperor Wuzong of the Tang Dynasty, Lü Yan (or Lü Dongbin), son of the regional inspector of Quzhou, went to the capital twice to take the imperial examination, but he failed both times. One day, on his way to Mount Huashan for sightseeing, he entered a wineshop. Before long, he saw a man with a long beard and green eyes coming from the west. Finding that Lü Yan was alone, the weird-looking man invited Lü Yan to eat with him. When the man went to the kitchen to prepare food in person Lü Yan fell asleep.

In a dream he was successful in the imperial examination. Whenever the emperor questioned him, he gave answers without hesitation. The emperor spoke highly of him. He entered the Hanlin Academy, and was promoted to prime minister. Everything went smoothly for him during his 30-year official career. However, one day he offended the emperor and was exiled to the south. In the face of wind, snow, frost and rain, all his followers and horses died on the way, leaving him alone. He sighed with sadness....

Lü Yan suddenly woke up, to find that the long-bearded man was still cooking the meal. The man looked at Lü Yan and sang:

The pot of millet is still cooking on the fire;
While you have been to Paradise in your dream.

"How do you know I had a dream?" Lü Yan asked in surprise.

The long-bearded man said, "You should not be pleased at being a high-ranking official in your dream; nor be sad for still being poor after you wake up. The life of a person is like a dream. Being rich and high in rank is a good dream; and being poor and lowly is a bad dream. Living a long life is a good dream; and dying young because of illness is a nightmare. High rank is only undeserved reputation; and wealth is like an evil fire. Gold, silver, pearls and treasures are external things; and even your sons and grandsons are only the people who come after you. Taoists, Heaven, earth and kings—care nothing for these. What can last for ever?"

Lü Yan suddenly saw the light. He fell to his knees before the stranger, saying, "Sir, you are not an ordinary person. Could you please tell me your name?"

The long-bearded man answered, "I'm a carefree person by the name of Han Zhongli. I live on Mount Zhongnan. If you can understand my words, we shall meet someday in Mount Zhongnan."

Then Lü Yan gave up his official career, took Han Zhongli as his teacher, and roamed among famous mountains and rivers.

Han Zhongli was also one of the Eight Immortals.

Qixu Pays a Visit to Zhichuan

A monk by the name of Li Qixu had been keen on Buddhism since his childhood. His father was a censor during the Kaiyuan reign period (713-741) of the Tang Dynasty. At the age of 20, he became a monk in a Buddhist temple in Chang'an. When the An Lushan rebellion broke out, and Emperor Xuan Zong fled to Sichuan, Qixu sought refuge in the Taibai Mountains, where he ate cypress leaves to survive. Later, he met a white-haired Taoist whose surname was Qiao. This man said to Qixu: "You were born an extraordinary person—proud, aloof, tall, straight and graceful. You are destined to visit Fairyland in the future."

Qixu made a few modest remarks. Taoist Qiao continued, "Some day you will meet a pedlar carrying a basket on his back on Mount Shangshan. You must reward him with food and drink. When the pedlar asks you: 'What do you want, Master?' You may reply: 'I want to pay a visit to Zhichuan.' Then he will take you there."

After the rebellion was put down, and Emperor Xuan Zong returned to the capital, the country was peaceful. Qixu went to live on Mount Shangshan (in present-day Shangxian County, Shaanxi Province). Qixu always offered free food and drink to pedlars. Within only a few months, he had done this favor for several hundred pedlars, but none of them asked him any questions. Qixu thought he had been deceived by the Taoist. When he was about to return to Chang'an, he met a young pedlar. This man asked him where he wanted to go. Qixu replied that he longed to go to Zhichuan. The pedlar was surprised: "Zhichuan is Fairyland; how can you go there?"

Qixu replied, "A friend of mine suggested that I go to Zhichuan. However, I don't know the way there."

"Let's go together. I guarantee that you'll reach Zhichuan," the pedlar said.

Following the pedlar, Qixu crossed mountain after mountain before coming to a cave. There was water flowing from the cave. Qixu and the pedlar blocked the water with stones. It took them three days.

Inside the cave, it was too dark to see anything. After walking a long way, they found the door of the cave. They pushed open the door, and found a beautiful, sunny land, with green mountains and sparkling waters. They walked on until they came to a high mountain with steep cliffs and winding paths. Qixu, who felt dizzy, dared not go on. The pedlar advised him: "Fairyland is not far from here. Please don't shrink from continuing."

239

The pedlar held Qixu's hand as they climbed the mountain. They came to a gigantic tree, with leaves growing luxuriantly. The pedlar climbed the tree fearlessly. A rope with a basket tied to it came snaking down from the top of the mountain. The pedlar and Qixu got into the basket, and closed their eyes. In an instant, they arrived at the top of the mountain, and there they found a city with palaces, towers and pavilions. The pedlar pointed to a place in the clouds: "That is Zhichuan!" he cried.

A celestial appeared and asked the pedlar: "Where does the monk come from?"

"This monk has longed to come to Zhichuan for a long time to settle a matter that has been weighing on his mind."

Qixu entered a hall, where there was a man sitting cross-legged. The pedlar introduced him to Qixu: "This is the true man of Zhichuan."

The true man looked Qixu up and down, and then asked, "Have you broken off relations with Sanpeng?"

Qixu was at a loss to understand what he meant.

The true man said, "This man does not understand Taoism. He should not stay here."

Then he made the pedlar take Qixu to the Cuihua Pavilion. A man was sleeping there, his shirt unbuttoned. His hair was more than 10 meters long, and his skin was black and shining. The pedlar said to Qixu: "This is Yang Wailang. He entered the mountains during the Sui Dynasty

(581-918), and cultivated himself according to the Taoist doctrines. After having pondered deeply, he is disillusioned with the mortal world."

All of a sudden, the man opened his bright piercing eyes. He stared at Qixu for a while without speaking. There was another man lying on the ground by the stone wall.

"This is Mr. Yiyou Ren. He is also a Taoist," the pedlar explained to Qixu.

After touring Zhichuan, the pedlar took Qixu back to earth, in accordance with the true man's order. On the way, Qixu asked the pedlar: "When the true man asked me about Sanpeng, I did not know how to answer, as I knew nothing about him."

The pedlar replied, "Sanpeng is the surname of Sanshi. Sanpeng always lives in the bodies of human beings, trying to find out their faults, and destroy them. On the day of Gengshen every year, Sanpeng enumerates a man's faults and reports them to Heaven. Without getting rid of Sanshi, Taoists cannot become immortals, and will try in vain to cultivate themselves."

A few days later, they returned to Qinchuan. Qixu and the pedlar became good friends, and hated to part with each other.

Soon after Qixu returned from Zhichuan, he went to the Taibai Mountains to live in seclusion. He never mentioned his visit to Zhichuan. During the Zhenyuan reign period (785-804), he moved to Mount Huashan. Zheng Shen of Xingyang and

Shen Yu of Wuxing once ran into Qixu when they walked from the capital and passed the mountain. They found that Qixu did not have a kitchen and did not eat any grain. Zheng Shen, who was very surprised to see this, made detailed inquiries. Qixu then told him about Zhichuan. One year later, when Zheng Shen passed that way again, he paid a special visit to Qixu. However, there was no sight of the hermit, and no one knew where he had gone.

Subduing the Goddesses
and Producing Salt

Zhang Ling, also known as Zhang Daoling (?-156), was the founder of the Doctrine of the Five Pecks of Rice. He was known as Heavenly Master Zhang. One day, when he took a tour with his disciples Wang Chang and Zhao Sheng he saw white vapor rising to the sky from Mount Yangshan. He turned to his disciples, and said, "It seems there are evildoers there. Let's go and take a look."

They climbed the mountain and saw 12 evil goddesses on the top. Zhang Ling scolded them in great anger. The goddesses replied, "We are the spirits of the land."

Zhang Ling paused for a while before asking, "Then do you know where a salt well is located?"

The goddesses said, "Not far from here is a pond where an evil dragon lives."

Zhang Ling went to the pond and summoned the dragon with a magic incantation. When the dragon refused to appear, Zhang Ling threw a talisman into the sky, which turned into a golden phoenix wheeling in the air over the pond. The frightened dragon ran away from the pond, the water in the pond dried up. When Zhang Ling went to taste the water he found it very salty. He then boiled the water and got salt. The golden phoenix went to dwell on South Mountain, which was thereafter named Phoenix Terrace.

While Zhang Ling was boiling water to get salt, a hunter approached him. Zhang Ling made him swear that he would not kill animals from then on, and taught him how to make salt. The salt well was about 180 meters deep and 3.3 meters wide. More than 40 bags of salt could be made at one time, promising great profits. The people of central Sichuan were very grateful to Zhang Ling for his gift of the salt well, and named the place after him—Lingzhou Prefecture. Moreover, by each salt well in Sichuan there is a shrine to Zhang Ling. As Zhang Ling subdued the evil goddesses with a talisman, they named it the "Ghost-Expelling Tally." Legend has it that when a well dries up, the talisman can be seen at the bottom. Copies of such talismans are used by the local people to drive away ghosts and evil influences.

The God of the East China Sea

One day Fei Changfang, a Taoist of the Eastern Han Dynasty (25-220), became acquainted with Mr. Kettle. On the following day, Fei paid a visit to Mr. Kettle, who led him into his kettle. Inside the kettle were gorgeous halls, where wine and delicious food were prepared. Fei Changfang and the old man drank their fill before leaving the kettle. The old man said to him: "I'm a celestial in Heaven. I was sent to the lower world because I had made some mistakes. My term of exile will expire soon, when I shall go back to Heaven. There is some wine downstairs. Let's drink the wine as our farewell banquet!"

Fei Changfang sent a dozen servants to fetch the wine jar. Even with their joint strength, they could not move it, but Mr. Kettle lifted it with one finger, and brought it upstairs. The two men drank wine from morning to evening, but there was still wine left in the jar.

After having learned magic powers from Mr. Kettle, Fei Changfang came to Runan, where there was an evil spirit. The spirit often turned himself into an apparition of the governor wearing his official costume and appeared in front of the local government residence, beating a drum. The local people were terrified of him, but could do nothing. One day, when the spirit appeared again, he ran into Fei Changfang who happened to be paying a visit to the governor. Seeing Fei Changfang, the spirit was so frightened that he took off his official robes, and fell to his knees, begging Fei Changfang to spare his life. Fei Changfang scolded him and made him show his true features. It turned out to be a soft-shelled turtle as large as a wheel. Fei Changfang took out a letter and told the turtle to deliver it to Lord Gepo. The old turtle kowtowed to him, and left with tears running down its cheeks. When he reached Lord Gepo, he put the letter on the ground, and took his own life. After the Dragon King of the East China Sea learned about this, he went to see Lord Gepo. Lord Gepo showed him Fei Changfang's letter, and the Dragon King had nothing to say.

After that, the Dragon King became a friend of Lord Gepo, and frequently visited his home. However the Dragon King was evil. He raped Lord Gepo's wife. Upon learning of this, Fei Changfang put the Dragon King in jail for three years, using his magic powers. Later, Fei Changfang went to the east coast, where he found that the place was suffering from a drought and the local people were praying for rain. Fei Changfang said to the people: "The Dragon King of the East China Sea is imprisoned in Gepo by me because he committed a crime. I'll excuse him and let him summon rain for you." After the Dragon King came out of the prison, he caused rain to fall, and the drought ceased. Then Fei Changfang submitted a memorial to the Jade Emperor and had the Dragon King escorted to the Heavenly court for interrogation.

Ascending a Height on the Double Ninth Festival

Huan Jing, a fellow townsman of Fei Changfang of Runan (in the southwest of Shangcai, Henan Province), learnt Taoist magic from Fei. One day Fei Changfang said to him: "On the Double Ninth Festival, on the ninth day of the ninth lunar month, your family will be faced with imminent disaster. You should get your family to make a red bag, put fruit of medicinal cornel in it and then ascend a height to drink chrysanthemum wine. In this way your family will avoid the disaster." Huan Jing did as he was told. He climbed a hill with his family members, and returned home in the evening. Upon returning home, he found that all his chickens and dogs had died. The customs of ascending a height on the Double Ninth Festival, inserting the fruit of medicinal cornel in the door and drinking chrysanthemum wine have been handed down to modern times.

From *History of the Later Han Dynasty* • *Fei Changfang*

Three Brothers Become Immortals

In the early Han Dynasty (206 B.C.-A.D. 220), there was a native of Xianyang, Shaanxi Province, called Mao Ying. His ancestors were the descendants of the imperial family of the Zhou Dynasty (11th century-256 B.C.). Later, when the family moved to Maodi, they adopted the surname Mao. His grandfather Mao Jia was named Duke Guangxin by Prince Zhuangxiang of the Qin Dynasty (221-206 B.C.). Mao Zuo, the sixth son of Mao Jia, was not interested in an official career, education, fame and wealth; he devoted all his life to farming. Mao Ying was the eldest son of Mao Zuo, born in the fifth year of the reign of Emperor Jing (145 B.C.).

Mao Ying was very brilliant in his childhood. He showed great interest in Taoism. At the age of 18, he went to Mount Hengshan and devoted himself to the study of *The Fundamental Text of Taoism* and *Commentary on the Book of Changes*. While studying in the mountains for over six years, Mao Ying ate only medicinal herbs and drank only spring water. He studied the Taoist doctrines every day. Later, he took a certain Mr. Wang as his teacher, and learnt Taoist magic from him. Twenty years later, when Mao Ying returned home, his father cursed him, saying, "You are not a filial son. You spent your time learning those mysterious magic arts rather than staying close to your parents and showing respects for us. You left home to roam about. You're not my son any more."

So saying, his father lifted a stick, intending to hit Mao Ying. To his surprise, the stick broke into dozens of pieces, which stuck in the walls.

When Emperor Xuan (reigned 73-49 B.C.) was in power, Mao Ying's two younger brothers pursued official careers. Mao Zhong was appointed Director of the Five Offices, and governor of Xihe; and Mao Gu, the chamberlain of the imperial insignia. When Mao Ying was leaving home for the second time, he said to his neighbors: "Though I am not destined to be a high-ranking official, I'll have a post in the Lingtai Fairyland. If you want to see if my words are true or not, come here on the third day of the fourth lunar month next year."

On the appointed day, the local people gathered in front of Mao Ying's home. Mao Ying said to them: "Most immortals do not make it widely known when they go to Heaven. However, I let all of you come today so as to convince my two younger brothers, who are obsessed with wealth and power, to turn to Taoism."

So saying, Mao Ying disappeared.

Upon learning of this, Mao Zhong and Mao Gu believed that it was possible for them too to become immortals. So they resigned their posts, and returned home to practice Taoism.

Later, the story about the three Mao brothers was on everybody's lips.

From *Records of Mount Maoshan*

Kou Qianzhi, a Taoist Master of North China

Kou Qianzhi (365-448), a native of Changping in Shanggu, was nearly three meters tall when he was only 16 years old. He was not interested in scholarly honor nor an official career, but concentrated on cultivating himself according to the Taoist doctrines.

At the age of 18, Kou Qianzhi hired a man by the name of Cheng Gongxing as his servant. One day, master and servant were working in the fields at the foot of the mountain. During a break, Kou Qianzhi had trouble setting up his divination board, until his servant showed him how to do it properly. Kou Qianzhi then knew that Cheng Gongxing was not an ordinary person.

Several months later, Cheng Gongxing said to Kou Qianzhi: "If you are determined to practice Taoism, you may come into the mountains with me." Qianzhi was very happy, and went to Mount Huangshan with him. Cheng Gongxing gave Qianzhi medicinal herbs to eat, after which he never felt hungry again.

After several years had elapsed, Cheng Gongxing said to Kou Qianzhi: "I am going to leave the mountain for a few days. You may continue to cultivate yourself here. If a person comes to give you some medicine, you may take it. Be sure to keep that in mind."

A few days later, an old Taoist brought some medicine to the mountain. Qianzhi treated him with due respect, and put the medicine aside. After having seen the Taoist off, Qianzhi returned to the cave. When he was about to take the medicine, he found that it was so foul that he could not bear to take it. When Cheng Gongxing returned, Kou Qianzhi told him what had happened.

Gongxing sighed, and said, "You've missed a good chance. You might have become an immortal if you had taken the medicine. However, you abandoned it, so you can only be a Taoist master."

From then on, Kou Qianzhi stayed on Mount Songshan practicing Taoism, and never left.

Later, Kou Qianzhi transformed the Taoist doctrines, cleared up and rectified Taoist organizations and founded new doctrines. He occupied an important position in the history of the development of Taoism.

From *Records of Shilao* • *History of Wei*

Xu Xun Kills the Flood Dragon

Xu Xun (?-374), styled Jingzhi, lived in the Jin Dynasty (265-420). He was well versed in economics, history, the various schools of thought, astronomy, geography, temperament and the five elements (metal, wood, water, fire and earth). He was particularly keen on Taoism. He was a good friend of the famous scholars Wu Meng and Guo Pu. They often visited renowned mountains together. Later Xu Xun served as magistrate of Jingyang County, enjoying a high reputation during his term of office. Later he resigned his post, and lived in seclusion because of political turmoil.

One day, Xu Xun and Wu Meng went to Songyang, where they learned that there was a female Taoist with great skills living in Danyang County. Her name was Chen Mu.

Chen Mu was very glad to see them. She said, "Finally, you have come. Not long ago, an immortal told me that I may pass on my skills to you." Then she taught Xu Xun how to kill demons with a sword.

Later, Xu Xun paid a visit to Xi'an County, where the local people were suffering greatly from the depredations of an evil spirit. But no one knew where the evil spirit hid himself. Xu Xun, who was determined to kill the spirit for the people, tried hard to find it. One day, he met three old men, whom he asked about the spirit. One of the old men said that an evil dragon was living under a bridge not far away. Xu Xun went to the bridge, raised his sword, the evil dragon ran away immediately. Xu Xun was upset that the dragon had escaped. So he told his other disciples to guard the mountain while he went in pursuit of it, together with Shi Ling and Gan Zhan.

In the sixth year of the Yongjia reign period of Emperor Huai (312), the trio reached Juncheng, near Changsha, where they met a beautifully dressed and handsome young man. The young man was refined and courteous. He told Xu Xun that his surname was Shen. When talking with him, Xu Xun found he answered fluently. After the young man left, Xu Xun said to his disciples: "That handsome young man is none other than the dragon spirit we have been looking for." His two disciples did not believe it, but acting according on their master's order, the two disciples chased after the young man, and asked him some questions. The young man treated them politely, but the two noticed an offensive smell coming from him. So they and Xu Xun followed him without being seen, trying to find out where he lived. A few days later they saw a yellow ox lying on the outskirts of the city. Xu Xun cut out a black paper ox and threw it into the air. The black ox fought with the yellow ox. Shi Ling and Gan Zhan ran after the ox with swords in hand. Injured by the swords, the yellow ox ran into a well in the south of the city, and then to a dry well in the residence of Jia Yi, a distinguished family in Changsha, turned into a handsome young man and entered the Jia Mansion.

It turned out that a few years before, when the dragon spirit had been chased by Xu Xun, he escaped to Changsha and turned into a young man. Jia Yu was very fond of the handsome and talented young man, and married his daughter to him. Now he lived in the Jia residence and had two sons. The evil dragon often took trips when summer was changing into autumn on the excuse of doing business. Each time when he returned, he brought a boatful of precious goods with him. All the family members trusted him.

The Jias were surprised to see the young man back wounded. When they asked him what had happened, the evil dragon replied, "I was attacked by robbers, who stole my goods and wounded me in the thigh." Jia Yu lost no time sending for a doctor. Upon learning this, Xu Xun disguised himself as a doctor and went to the Jia residence. Jia Yu summoned his son-in-law to come out to see the doctor. The evil dragon dared not appear, so, together with Jia Yu, Xu Xun chased the dragon and killed it.

Legend has it that Xu Xun became an immortal in Jiangxi and was called Xu True Man.

From *History of the Jin Dynasty*

Xu Xiyan Meets Immortals

Xu Xiyan, a native of Qishan (present-day Qixian County, Shaanxi Province), passed the imperial examinations at the county and provincial levels. However, he failed at the highest-level regular civil service recruitment examination. He went to live at the Wuyun Taoist Temple for the time being. One day, when he was about to hasten home for the funeral of a parent, he went to a market to select a horse. He looked at three horses, but none of them satisfied him. Suddenly he saw a barbarian leading a horse. Xiyan was not sure if it was a good one or not, but the abbot of the temple, who was with him, said, after having examined it: "You will benefit greatly if you buy this horse." He continued, "It is a horse of a fine breed."

No one at the market believed the abbot's words. However, Xiyan took his advice, and bought it. On the way to Jiange, the horse panicked and fell down into a deep valley. Fortunately it fell upon a thick layer of dried leaves; neither the horse nor Xiyan were injured. However, the valley was pitch-dark. They stayed in the valley for a night, before finding a stone crack, through which they came to a place with peach blossoms in full bloom. Among the peach trees there lay a pond surrounded by green stones. There was a stone house by the pond. Xiyan led the horse to the stone house, and found inside it a Taoist with white hair at his temples and rosy cheeks lying on a bed, attended by two beautiful girls.

Xiyan entered the stone house, and bowed to the Taoist. When the girls asked him where he was from, Xiyan told them of his experience. The girls conveyed Xiyan's story to the Taoist, whose name was Master Yuan. The latter summoned him to his bedside, and asked, "Do you have any hobbies?"

Xiyan replied, "I love to read the books by Zhuang Zi and Lao Zi and others on Taoism."

Master Yuan said, "You are about to attain enlightenment; our meeting today is the will of Heaven."

At this moment, the two girls came to report that an abbot was asking for an interview. The abbot was invited in and asked to take a seat. Xiyan found the newcomer had a large mouth, and an ancient and unsophisticated appearance. Master Yuan Qun asked, "Why did you come so far to see me today?"

"I came to pay a special visit to you," the abbot replied.

Then Master Yuan introduced the abbot to Xiyan. Looking at him closely, Xiyan was surprised to find that he was none other than the Taoist who had persuaded him to buy the horse. Xiyan went up to kowtow to him. As he did so, a boy came to report to Master Yuan: "The Dragon King of the East Sea invites Master Yuan to appreciate the moon with him on Mount Longshan." Master Yuan let Xiyan go with him. Riding deer, they swiftly arrived at Mount Longshan. Xiyan found it was indeed a fairyland surrounded by clouds and mist. Master Yuan introduced Xiyan to the Dragon King, who said, "You're the Aide Xu's grandson."

Xiyan said, "My parents died a long time ago. I don't know anything about my grandfather."

The Dragon King replied, "Last night, I drank wine with your grandfather. He will come today, too." Then the Dragon King had wine served.

When Master Yuan asked the Dragon King how deep the sea was, he replied, "The sea is only half as deep as it was when we met last time."

The Dragon King had a banquet served, and asked the girls to sing a song for Master Yuan. The Dragon King, Master Yuan and Xiyan then drank wine and sang songs. After the banquet, Master Yuan and Xiyan took their leave, and returned to Yuan's residence in the cave, riding the deer. Soon afterwards Xiyan bowed to Master Yuan, and took his leave.

Master Yuan sent one of the maidens to lead out Xiyan's horse. Master Yuan pointed to the horse, and said to Xiyan: "Though the horse belongs to you, it was originally a dragon living in my cave.

Having a fierce temper, he once trampled my crops without any reason. So I sent it to the lower world. You're linked with the horse by fate. So it came to help you."

He continued, "After you return to the world, the horse will no longer be of any use to you. You may untie it by the river, and it will turn into a dragon and come back."

Xiyan thereupon mounted the horse and departed.

Tall Immortal Hu

During the reign of Emperor Gaozong (reigned 650-683) of the Tang Dynasty, a man by the name of Hu Huichao lived in Shandong. In his forties, he had a long beard and posed as a person of high morals. He did not look very tall, but when he stood next to anyone else, he was always one head taller. Many people vied with him to see who was taller, and always coming second. Both puzzled and surprised, the people called him Tall Immortal Hu. When Hu Huichao was asked about his age, he always said he was 52 years old. But an old man who had known Hu Huichao for dozens of years said that he had been 52 years old many years previously.

One day Tall Immortal Hu passed by a thick clump of grass, and noticed several bones in it. Hu told the passers-by that there were pearls, cultural relics and other treasures buried in that spot. The passers-by did not believe him. So Hu said: "If you don't believe me, try digging there." The people got some tools and began to dig. After having dug three meters down, several treasures were discovered.

The local people then admired him very much, and called him "Taoist Master."

Outside the city proper there was a Taoist temple, called the Youwei Temple. It was old and shabby. Hu Huichao went there one day, and asked the abbot why it was so dilapidated. The abbot replied, "The temple was built in the early Tang Dynasty. With the passage of time, it has long been out of repair. Without donations from pilgrims, we are not able to have it repaired."

Upon hearing this, Hu Huichao said: "Don't worry about it. I'll do my best to help you."

One month later, Taoist Master Hu had a raft full of timber transported to the outlet of the river, 45 km from the temple. At nightfall, Taoist Master Hu murmured to himself. All of a sudden, there came a rainstorm accompanied by thunder and lightning. Early the next morning, the timber was found arranged in good order in front of the temple. The abbot and monks were greatly surprised. They bowed to Taoist Master Hu to express their gratitude to him. However, they still needed money to employ artisans to have the temple repaired. Hu Huichao took them to a huge rock and said, "The money for repairing the temple is under this rock. You can dig it up."

The abbot, half believing and half doubting, ordered the monks to dig there. They found a cave under the rock, which held a huge hoard of coins, enough to have the temple renovated. A few months later, the temple was repaired. It looked magnificent, with upturned eaves and painted pillars. Taoist Master Hu also had three wells dug in front of the temple, to be used in case of fire.

Later, Emperor Gaozong summoned Taoist Master Hu to his palace. However Hu Huichao insisted that he should not stay in the palace, but promised he would make a pill of immortality in the mountains and present it to the emperor. A few years later, he did so, much to the delight of the emperor.

Absolute Sincerity

During the reign of Emperor Ruizong (reigned 710-712) of the Tang Dynasty, Tang Ruoshan served as deputy imperial secretary, and later imperial secretary. In the Kaiyuan reign period (713-741) of Emperor Xuanzong, he served as prefect of Runzhou Prefecture. His younger brother was Tang Ruishui, a Taoist of the Hengshan Taoist Temple. As he was once instructed by the god of the Taiyuan Valley, he was often summoned to the palace to explain Taoism. Influenced by his younger brother, Tang Ruishan was also interested in Taoism. Wherever he went, he would make friends with alchemists and treat them with due respect even if he could not learn any skills from them.

One day, an old and feeble man came to call on him. The old man said he knew the way to live a long life. The people around laughed, thinking the somebody so feeble could not possibly know how to live a long life. However, Ruoshan invited him respectfully to live in his house. At first, when Ruoshan discussed pills of immortality with him, he kept his mouth shut, only smiling at Ruoshan.

One month later, the old man said, "It is very costly for you to support nearly 100 people every day. Though you're a local prefect, you are not wealthy. I know you often run short of money. How can you support such a big family? Moreover, you have diverted a large amount of silver from the warehouse. What will you do when that fact is discovered?"

Ruoshan, who was astonished to hear this, hid his agitation as he said, "I shall find a way out soon. Unfortunately, I haven't got a good plan now. If I am punished, I'll make no complaints. But all my household, nearly 100 people, will suffer from hunger and cold without knowing the reason." Ruoshan, however, was overcome with sadness.

The old man burst out laughing: "Don't worry," he said. Please have some wine and dishes prepared, and we'll have a meal together."

Though in low spirits, Ruoshan had to keep him company. Usually Ruoshan did not drink wine. On this occasion, though, acting out of character, Ruoshan drank one cup after another. Soon he felt dizzy, but he dared not leave the table, and kept drinking wine with the old man until the moon rose. The old man then helped Ruoshan into the room where he made pills of immortality. Upon entering the room, the old man made Ruoshan take out the medicinal materials, and told the servants to build a stove. Then he made Ruoshan and the others sit with their backs to the stove. He took two small pills out of a small bottle gourd and threw them into the stove. All of a sudden, flames roared. Then he sealed the stove. After that he led Ruoshan and the others out of the room, and locked the door.

Ruoshan looked at the old man, puzzled.

The old man explained to him: "You have a gentle disposition; you do not get angry or hold grudges. The immortals respect your personality. You have dedicated yourself to making pills of immortality, so I came to give you a hand. Now, in the stove there are two portions of gold and silver. Leave one portion to your descendants and the poor, and the other portion shall be put in the warehouse. You don't have any problems at home, so you should come with me to take a boat trip. Tomorrow we shall meet in the middle of the river. Please don't forget."

Early the next morning, Ruoshan did indeed find gold and silver in the stove. He thereupon sealed the stove and locked the room. Then he went to the rear hall and gather his household there. After a brief talk to them, he took his guests and colleagues on board a boat. When the boat was moving between the Jinshan and Jiaoshan hills (northwest of Zhenjiang, Jiangsu Province), the river was suddenly covered with dense fog. Ruoshan saw the old man in a small boat approaching one side of his own boat. He jumped into the small boat, and went away with the old man. Soon the dense fog disappeared, and the sun shone again. When the people in the boat found that Ruoshan had disappeared, they were frightened. They entered the cabin, and saw a letter on the table, which turned out to be a memorial to the throne, resigning his post.

A Trip to Xichuan

Ma Xiang, styled Ziran, lived in Yanguan County. Both his grandfather and father were local officials. Ma Xiang was keen on history and literature, and good at Taoist magic arts. But no one knew who his teacher was.

One day, the magistrate sent him to Xichuan (present-day Chengdu in Sichuan Province) on business. As Xichuan was more than 500 km from Yanguan, it would be an arduous journey. Ma Xiang did not want to go, but he dared not disobey the order of the magistrate. On the first day, Ma Xiang walked about a dozen km. At nightfall, he met a Taoist, and the two walked together for about half an hour. By that time, it was quite dark.

"This is the first day of your trip, so you cannot be very tired; why don't we walk all night?" the Taoist suggested.

"We have a long way to go; it does not matter to us if we get there one day earlier or later. Why don't we put up at an inn for the night?" Ma Xiang replied.

"But we can get to Xichuan by walking all night," the Taoist said with a smile.

"Please don't tease me. Xichuan is about 500 kilometers from here. How can we get there in one night?" Ma Xiang protested.

"Why should I make fun of you? We can get to Xichuan early tomorrow, doing it my way."

"May I ask what is your way?"

"It is faster to go by boat," the Taoist replied.

"That's not right. Traveling by boat is much slower than by land. In addition, there is no river here; how can we go there by boat?" Ma Xiang objected.

Pointing at a well, the Taoist said, "Is there water in the well?"

When the Taoist found that Ma Xiang did not understand him, he said, "If you don't agree, I'll go by myself." So saying, he jumped into the well.

Ma Xiang stepped forward to stop him, but it was already too late. Looking into the well, he found that there was no sight of the Taoist. He stared blankly for a while, then shouted down the well. There was no answer. Then he sat by the well, lost in thought. All of a sudden, he realized that the Taoist must be an immortal, who had played some magic trick. He suddenly fell into the well and lost consciousness.

At daybreak, Ma Xiang found himself lying in front of the *yamen* (government office) of Xichuan. The Taoist was sitting by him, smiling. When Ma Xiang tried to get up, the Taoist pressed him down, and said, Don't hurry. You may get up after you recover."

Ma Xiang insisted on getting up. He fell down on knees, and asked the Taoist to take him as his disciple. The Taoist agreed.

Unlucky Immortal

Wang Changyu, a native of Zizhou Prefecture in Sichuan, was a judge. One day, he put some stewed pig's trotters in a kitchen cupboard for his supper. His wife moved the pig's trotters to another place without telling him. At nightfall, when supper was served, Wang Changyu told the maid Honglian to take out the pig's trotters from the cupboard. When the maid said that she could not find them, Wang Changyu flew into a rage, thinking that she had eaten them. Honglian denied the charge, and Wang Changyu beat her with a bamboo whip.

At this moment, Wang Changyu's wife took out the pig's trotters, saying, "I took them away to see how you would treat the matter. Don't you try cases in this way?"

Wang Changyu felt ashamed, not knowing what to say. From then on, he tried cases with great care, and persisted in correcting all misjudged cases, and upholding justice.

One day, a Taoist known as the Unlucky Immortal, fell down drunk in the street. Now, it happened that the local military commander had ordered that a strict curfew be observed, and that anyone breaking it be put to death. When Wang Changyu was leading a night patrol, he found the drunken Taoist. Wang helped him up and took him to his own home. To his surprise, when the Taoist woke up, he started to call out Wang Changyu's name over and over again. He then said, "I had three taels of gold and 2,000 coins in my two bags. But they are all gone. It must have been you who took my money."

Instead of arguing with him, Wang Changyu gave him exactly that amount of money. The Taoist then stood up and took his leave: "We'll meet again some day in Luzhou," he promised.

A few years later, Wang Changyu was escorting a consignment of silk to Luzhou. He knew that for some reason the amount of silk was inadequate, and he expected to be thrown into prison. As they neared Jiang'an, two armed men sprang out in front of them. Wang Changyu was so scared that he trembled all over and dared not move. But one of the two men said to him: "Don't be afraid. I'm Unlucky Immortal."

Then he took Wang Changyu by the hand to his residence, and threw a banquet for him. During the banquet, the Unlucky Immortal presented Wang Changyu with money and silk, which he said was to repay him for his kindness of a few years previously. Wang Changyu was overjoyed. He accepted the money and silk, and accomplished his task without any problem.

Wang Changyu went back to see the Taoist in Jiang'an. The latter told him: "Now I will tell you the secret of making elixirs. You may go back afterwards and make elixirs, cultivate yourself."

Upon returning to his hometown, Wang Changyu submitted his resignation. Then he went to Mount Changping to cultivate himself.

Zhang Bai in Wuling

Zhang Bai, styled Xubai, called himself Baiyunzi. During the Kaibao reign period (968-976) of Emperor Taizu of the Song Dynasty, wars broke out frequently. During his tour of Wuling (present-day Changde in Hunan Province), Governor Liu Chi and Military Supervisor Zhang Yanfu treated him with great respect. So Zhang Bai presented a book on the way to keep in good health to Zhang Yanfu, urging him to take care of his health according to the instructions in the book.

Zhang Bai, good at concealing his true features, was often given to heavy drinking. Dead drunk, he would curse those whom he met in the street. Believing he was a madman, the passer-by did not take his words seriously.

One day, Zhang Bai went to the Cuis' wineshop. After he had drunk many large cups of wine, the proprietor asked Zhang Bai to pay. A waiter, who thought it was unfair, cut in: "Though the Taoist is good at drinking wine. However as a tremendous drinker, he has attracted lots of customers for us. You have earned lots of money because of him; how can you ask him to pay?"

Convinced, the proprietor gave up. From that day on, whenever Zhang Bai walked into the wineshop, the proprietor would supply him with free wine. A few days later, the proprietor found a poem written on the wall of his shop. It read:

By the Wuling Stream sits the Cuis' wineshop.
This wineshop should not be on earth, but in Heaven.
After a Taoist from the south has got drunk there,
He lies at the entrance of the White Cloud Cave.

After that, the wineshop's business became more brisk.

Tang Yunsheng and Wei Yingshi from Mount Hengshan, who had admired Zhang Bai for quite a long time, often invited him to travel round the country with them. Zhang Bai was very intelligent, and had a facile imagination. Within a few days he wrote 300 poems, each starting with the sentence "In scenic Wuling in spring." For instance:

In scenic Wuling in spring
There are twelve wineshops.
I never turn my head before I get drunk.
And I'm too lazy to nod to others.
I don't care about rights and wrongs,
And have nothing to do with fame and gain.
With my hat on my head,
I drift with the tide.

All of his poems contain reflections of his philosophy of life.

A Mental Trip to Yangzhou

Zhang Boduan (984-1082) was a native of Tiantai (now in Zhejiang Province). In his childhood he studied avidly, and knew Confucianism, Taoism and Buddhism well. He served as a prefecture-level official. Later, he made a trip around Sichuan, where he adopted Yongcheng as his name, and styled himself Pingshu. He also adopted the alias of Ziyang. As the founder of the Ziyang school of Taoism, he wrote the essay "Understanding Truth," which has spread far and wide.

A monk, who had practiced Buddhism hard for a long time, was very good at abstract meditation. After sitting for a moment, he could mentally cover several hundred *li*.

One day, Ziyang met the monk. They felt like old friends at their very first meeting. In the course of a most agreeable chat, they decided they make a mental trip to Yangzhou to appreciate *qionghua* (a rare flower said to confer immortality when eaten). So they entered a spotlessly clean room, sat down facing each other and began their mental trip to Yangzhou.

Upon arrival at Yangzhou, Ziyang found the

monk had already got there before him. After having walked around the flowers three times, Ziyang suggested, "Shall each of us pluck a flower for a souvenir?"

"That's a good idea," the monk agreed. Then each of them plucked a flower, and returned to where they had come from.

Soon afterwards, Ziyang and the monk woke up.

"Where's your flower, master?" Ziyang asked.

The monk was empty-handed, while Ziyang held two flowers. Then Ziyang said to the monk: "Practicing Buddhism is different from practicing Taoism, each having its own profound mystery. Is that right?"

The monk nodded in agreement. From then on, the two were bosom friends.

Later, when a disciple asked Ziyang why they had taken different attitudes toward plucking flowers, since Ziyang and the monk made a mental trip together to Yangzhou, Ziyang replied, "Buddhism focuses on training the mind, while Taoism stresses training the body. The former does not reveal the form, while the latter reveals the form. That's why the monk was empty-handed, but I held two flowers.

"Moreover, both Taoism and Buddhism emphasize the cultivation of body and mind. The monks who only cultivate the mind, rather than both mind and body are only regarded as second-class

Buddhists, or fifth-class spirits according to Taoism, who are shunned by Buddhists and immortals. People practicing Buddhism are generally classified into three types; and those practicing Taoism are divided into five classes and 3,600 categories. Immortal Zhongli once said, 'There are 3,600 categories of wonderful ways, each holding a way as the organ. However, the secret of becoming an immortal is not included in the 3,600 categories.' This means that if one wants to become an immortal or a Buddha, he or she must cultivate both mind and body."

Crossing a River on a Bamboo Hat

Chen Nan, styled Nanshu and Cuixu, was a native of Xiangshuiyan in Boluo County, Huizhou Prefecture. In the Song Dynasty (960-1279), he made a living by repairing buckets for others. He was very alert and resourceful, words flowing from his mouth as from the pen of a master.

In addition, Chen Nan was good at practicing traditional Chinese medicine. When he treated poor patients, he often made medicines out of soil, and they were very efficacious. Hence he earned the nickname of "Mud Ball Chen." During the Zhenghe reign period (1111-1118) of Emperor Huizong of the Song Dynasty, he went to Luofu. With his hair disheveled and in ragged clothes, he often came and went in a hurry. However, he always appeared in time to rescue people. For instance, one day, when he was passing through Cangwu, the area was suffering a severe drought. The local people kneeled down on the ground, praying to Heaven for rain. Chen Nan came to a deep pool, and waved an iron whip over it two to three times. All of a sudden, a huge dragon jumped out of the pool and flew up to the sky. Soon afterwards, dark clouds gathered, lightning flashed and thunder growled. It then rained cats and dogs. The local people were so grateful to Chen Nan that they kowtowed to him.

Chen Nan left Cangwu for Dayi. After having crossed three huge mountains, he found a big river blocking his way. The water ran so swiftly that no boat could sail across it. Chen Nan took off his bamboo hat, threw it into the river, jumped onto the hat and crossed the river in no time at all. No sooner had he gone ashore than a group of bandits blocked his way. Chen Nan made no resistance. The bandits killed him and buried him on the spot. However, three days later, Chen Nan was seen in Changsha, where he offended the military commissioner and was escorted to Yongzhou Prefecture. During his detention, Chen Nan sat quietly for three days and nights. When he was released, he spat some scraps of gold from his mouth and gave them to the poor.

Chen Nan determined to stay on earth 43 years. On the 14th day of the fourth lunar month of the sixth year of the Jiading reign period (1213) of Emperor Ningzong of the Song Dynasty, he attended the crane fair in Zhangzhou. After the fair, he disappeared, leaving a poem:

When thunder was heard in the sky,
I came to the earth with no trace.
Today I'll leave the earth
On a fire dragon without horns.

The Story of Zhu Ju

Zhu Ju, whose alias was Cuiyang, was a native of Anqing, Huaixi. When he was only six years old, his parents died. Zhu Ju was very intelligent. He studied Confucianism very hard, and was especially good at divination. After he had failed the imperial examination at the county level twice, he turned to study Buddhism and Taoism. One day he saw his shadow in a river, and was suddenly enlightened. He started to visit famous mountains and historical sites all over the country.

One day, Zhu Ju came to Boluo in Huizhou, where he saw a "madman" singing, with an orange in his hand: "Orange, orange, no one knows it, but a person whose surname is Zhu."

None of the people in the street understood what he was saying, but Zhu Ju understood. He followed him to the outskirts of the city, until they were quite alone. Zhu Ju kneeled on the ground, and asked, "Are you Immortal Ju Junzi?"

"Who are you? How do you know my name?" the man retorted.

Zhu Ju then told him his name, adding, "My

mother once told me that when she was pregnant a man by the name of Ju Junzi came to her home."

"That's right," the Taoist said with a smile. "What do you want then—money or an influential rank? You can have either."

Zhu Ju laughed, saying, "Wealth and rank are like waves in the sea or floating clouds in the sky, moving here and there. I have heard that you know the secret of how to prolong people's lives. Could you please tell me the secret?"

The Taoist remained silent. Zhu Ju begged him time and again, until finally the Taoist was moved by his sincerity.

"The so-called 'breath,' which comes from the 'heart' and 'vitality,' is the root of nihility and the master of good fortune. Rising and falling, separation and reunion, all come from 'one's own heart.' If a person can understand his or her own heart, he or she will understand his or her own temperament, and will be very close to becoming a sage. One who does not understand his or her own heart will not find the way to become an immortal."

Then he pointed to a huge rock in front of a mountain, and said: "You may come to see me there tomorrow."

At midnight of the following day, Zhu Ju went to the rock. Soon the Taoist arrived. He said to Zhu Ju, with satisfaction: "You've come at the right time. Go to Mount Wangong and build a hermitage, where you may cultivate yourself. The time will come when you will become an immortal."

Zhu Ju did as the Taoist instructed him. A few years later, he became an immortal.

A Painted Ox Eats Grass

Xu Fengyuan of Quzhou (in present-day Zhejiang Province) was very fond of making friends with Buddhist monks and Taoists. One day, when a Taoist by the name of Zhang Tan passed by Xu Fengyuan's home, Xu invited him in to have a chat and to stay the night. The Taoist looked poor. Although it was midwinter, he wore only a blue cloth Taoist robe, and his only possession was a bamboo flute. At the end of each month, he would go to the mountains to play the flute all night.

Xu Fengyuan was keen on divination. Every day, when night fell he would close the door and practice divination by himself. However though he spent much of his time in practicing mathematical calculations, he failed to grasp the main points. That particular evening Zhang Tan, who knew well that Xu Fengyuan was eager to learn divination, shouted from outside his room: "How can you a scholar know about divination? Let me teach you tomorrow."

The following day, Zhang Tan taught him the rules of divination.

It was said that a disciple of Zhang Tan had a

painting of an ox. One day Zhang Tan said to his friends: "If you hang the painting on a wall, and put a pile of grass by it, soon afterwards most of the grasses will have been eaten, and the ox from the painting will also have left a pile of dung."

His friends did not believe him, so Zhang Tan ordered his disciple to hang the painting on a wall, and place some grass by it. Then Zhang Tan began to murmur to himself. All of a sudden, the ox in the painting began to move and eat the grass. All onlookers gasped in amazement.

Madam Fan Prays for Rain

Madam Fan was a 12th-generation descendant of Fan Kuai. Also known as the Marquis of Wuyang, Fan Kuai had rendered outstanding service during the reign of Emperor Gaozu of Han, Liu Bang. Her maternal grandfather was Wang Xun, a 17th-generation descendant of Wang Qiao, who was the heir of King Ling (reigned 571-545 B.C.) of the Zhou Dynasty. Her mother died when Madam Fan was very young, and Madam Fan was raised by her maternal grandfather.

Madam Fan was fond of reading books in her childhood, and Wang Xun served as her teacher. When she was 13 years old, she started to study the classics by herself.

One day she met a young woman by a forest. The woman asked Madam Fan: "Do you want to learn Taoist magic?"

"Though I'm very young, I'm especially keen on Taoist magic," Madam Fan said.

The woman said, "I am an immortal, by the name of Ah Wangxiao. I came here to teach you Taoism. Whenever you have time, please come here, and I'll explain Taoism to you."

For two years, Madam Fan acted according to the female Taoist's instructions—going to the forest by herself every day to read books. Her maternal grandmother thought it was strange that her granddaughter went out every day. One day she followed her to the forest without being seen by her granddaughter. She was very happy to see her granddaughter reading books in the forests with another young girl. She went back home quietly, and kept it secret.

Three years later, Madam Fan had finished reading all the Taoist books, and mastered Taoist magic power.

During the reign of Emperor Weiwen (reigned 220-226), there was no rain for more than 70 days in succession, with the scorching sun directly overhead in a cloudless sky. Emperor Weiwen tried every method of praying for rain, but all in vain. One day, a local official recommended Madam Fan to the emperor, saying, "Wang Xun's granddaughter knows Taoist magic. It is certain that she can pray for rain effectively." Then the emperor let his consort, Zhao Dan, invite Madam Fan. At that time Madam Fan was not married, and she was too shy to show her face in public.

Zhao Dan said, "I grew up in the imperial family. However out of pity for all people of our country, I have to come to see you. Now the country is afflicted with a severe drought, and the people are suffering. Saving people from disaster is a good deed. Why don't you use your magic power to help the people?"

Upon hearing this, Madam Fan wrote a letter to the Dragon King, and had it sent to a deep pool. Soon afterwards it started raining.

Two years later, Madam Fan married a young man by the surname of Liu. When her husband was appointed as a local official, she left with her husband.

From *Gold Lock and Flowing Pearl*

图书在版编目（CIP）数据

中国神仙家故事选：英文 / 元央编. －北京：
外文出版社，2000
ISBN 978-7-119-02142-3

I. 中… II. 元… III. 故事－作品集－中国－当代－英文 IV.1247.8

中国版本图书馆 CIP 数据核字（1999）第 03522 号

责任编辑　吴灿飞
英文编辑　王增芬
封面设计　王　志
插图绘制　李士伋

中国神仙家故事选

元央　编

＊

© 2010外文出版社
外文出版社出版
（中国北京百万庄大街 24 号）
邮政编码：100037
网址:http://www.flp.com.cn
北京外文印刷厂印刷
中国国际图书贸易总公司发行
（中国北京车公庄西路35号）
北京邮政信箱第399号　邮政编码　100044
2000年第1版
2010年第1版第2次印刷
（英）
ISBN 978-7-119-02142-3
03500
10-E-3253P